THE ADVISOR
(Da Co-Van)

Porfirio Torres-Gonzales

VANTAGE PRESS
New York

In memory of my wife, Elsa A. Torres (Mayita)

Preface

Long before there was a fictitious character called Rambo, there was a true person called Da Co-Van, meaning "the Advisor" in Vietnamese.

This is a true story, although some of the names have been changed to protect people's rights and their identity.

Most of all the characters listed in this story were military personnel or individuals in some way connected or affected by military decisions or actions. These decisions had some impact on them as well as on the Advisor.

The most touched and affected by the events related or mentioned in this story was the Advisor, for he lived through all the experiences related here and they are part of his life.

As you read, you might question some of these events, but they are true, for the author was the Advisor himself, and he personally lived through every one of them.

1

In May 1958, a ship departed from a port in Honolulu, the capital city of the state of Hawaii. Honolulu is located on the island of Oahu, which is proud of its famous beach, Waikiki. Oahu is one of the seven islands of the Hawaiian archipelago.

After seven days and a very pleasant trip across the Pacific Ocean, the boat arrived at an Army terminal located in Oakland, California.

During the voyage there were no high waves or strong winds. The ocean waters were very calm throughout, and the skies were clear and star-spangled every night.

The ship, named *Leilani*, was a luxury liner on a dual mission of carrying vacationers as well as military dependents. Some of the dependents were accompanied by their sponsors.

The U.S. Department of Defense had a contract with civilian sea liners, and very frequently military personnel accompanying their dependents traveled, together with vacationers and visitors from many of the Pacific islands, to the United States and vice-versa.

Aboard the ship on this particular trip was an Army sergeant first class by the name of Porfirio Torres-Gonzales. Torres had completed a three-year tour while serving with the 25th Infantry Division. The division, nicknamed Tropical Lightning, had been stationed at Schofield Barracks almost since the Korean War's cease-fire was declared in 1953.

Sergeant Torres, who was drafted to serve during the Korean Conflict, had been in the military for eight years. He had been

1

studying to obtain a bachelor's degree in humanities at the University of Puerto Rico when Uncle Sam enlisted him on the 8th of June, 1951. Torres did not ask for a deferment and felt very proud to fulfill his obligations. His father had proudly served during World War I, and his two brothers had done the same during World War II. Besides, Torres was hoping to make a career out of the military.

Also aboard the ship, among three hundred other passengers, was Torres's family: his wife Elsa and their two-and-a-half-year-old daughter, Amy. Amy had been born at Presidio Army Hospital, located in San Francisco, California, when Elsa was on her way with her husband to visit Puerto Rico as compensation of a reenlistment leave Torres took after six months in Hawaii. Torres had secured traveling orders to return back to Hawaii when Elsa, who was seven months pregnant, delivered the baby upon her arrival in San Francisco. Even though premature, a very healthy baby girl was born February 5, 1956.

After the Torres family arrived in Oakland on their return trip to the mainland, they were to continue on to New York City. Torres was assigned to report to Fort Dix in New Jersey. They took an airline flight to Kennedy International Airport after a day at Oakland Army Terminal Guest House, where they stayed for the night. When the Torres family arrived at the airport in New York, they were greeted by Luis, an uncle-in-law of Elsa's. Luis was married to Dorcas, who was Elsa's aunt and who had been living in New York for some years.

Luis Colon and his wife had a one-bedroom apartment located on 25th Street on the west side of Manhattan. When Luis and the Torres family arrived, they looked for a hotel nearby and found one only two blocks away on 27th Street. It was a low-priced hotel, costing only $7 a night for a double bed, but it was clean and neat and had its own private bath in the room. It would do for the two nights they intended to stay in the Big Apple to visit and shop around.

Torres's car had been shipped from "the Rock" as the soldiers had nicknamed the island of Oahu. It had been forty-five days since it was loaded onto a commercial cargo ship bound to Bayonne Army Terminal in New Jersey.

Early the next morning, Luis came to pick up Torres and took him through the Lincoln Tunnel into New Jersey. They were going to pick up Torres's car from the terminal in Bayonne.

After securing the car, Torres followed Luis back into New York, and the families met for a late breakfast at the Colons' apartment. The Torres family was invited for lunch and supper, and both families intended to visit other families who also lived in New York.

Torres returned with his family to the hotel about 10:00 P.M. after a long day visiting Elsa's relatives and family friends. They were also invited by the Colons to have breakfast with them the next day.

Early the next morning, Torres walked down the stairs from the second floor. As he stepped outside, he noticed that his car was missing from the spot where he had parked it the previous night. In desperation, Torres glanced right and left up both sides of the street. It was then that he saw his car being hauled away by a tow truck, which was moving very quickly on the left side down the street.

Torres ran and tried to catch up with the truck, but it was already too far away. The truck turned left onto Columbus Avenue, which was the nearest street crossing 27th Street. If the truck driver saw Torres chasing him, he disregarded him and never slowed down for a second. All that came into Torres's mind was the meaning of the word *aloha*, which was printed on his car's license plate. *Aloha* has a dual meaning of "hello" and "good-bye," the latter being the most appropriate for what was happening to his car.

Torres thought someone was stealing the car and that in a city as big as New York it would never be found. The hotel's attendant, who had heard the commotion outside when Torres yelled to the driver of the tow truck, came out the front door to investigate what was going on. Immediately he knew what was happening and without hesitation called Torres and said to him, "You know, Sarge, they took your car because it was parked illegally. What I don't understand is why they did not start with the first car in line? Your car was in the middle of six cars." He pointed to the cars on each side of the empty space where Torres's car had been parked.

The attendant continued, "None of those cars are supposed to be here now. It's 9:15 A.M. and today is trash pick-up day. Frankly, I think they picked on your car because of the plates. It did not have New York plates; the others do." While he was pointing at them, he continued saying, "What a shame. You just arrived in New York and this had to happen to you." He scratched his head in disbelief.

The attendant walked toward the hotel's front door, then stepped back in Torres's direction and said, "Sarge, you probably have to go to some depot in Brooklyn to get your car back. That's where they take all the impounded cars. You'll have to pay a fine and tow costs too. Go inside and use the phone on top of my desk. Call a cab or someone in your family who has a car and try to get your car back as soon as possible. I hope they don't strip it before you get there. Sometimes they do, you know."

The old man continued to give advice and information to Torres. "Next time, check where you park your car. They have a system here in New York that they call alternate parking. Today, because it's trash pick-up day, no one is allowed to park on this side of the street. You can park on this side today after four o'clock in the afternoon. Tomorrow the same thing will happen on the other side. They worked fast this morning because normally they only start to haul cars after 10:00 A.M. They probably want to make more money for the city."

Torres followed the attendant inside the hotel. While the

old man was walking ahead of him, he checked his wallet for the piece of paper where he had Luis's phone number listed.

The attendant handed Torres the telephone and said, "Here, call your family or a cab. Hurry up. No charge for the telephone use; it's on the house. But call before they steal anything of value or strip the car. They may do it and then you won't be able to claim anything. They'll say that they picked the vehicle up in that condition and that it was probably ransacked during the night and you didn't know about it. You'll never be able to prove they did it; they know their tricks."

Torres did not waste any time but immediately dialed Luis's number. Luis was about to leave his apartment to drive to Bellevue Hospital, where he was going to pick up his paycheck. When Luis arrived at the hotel, Torres was waiting by the front door, having already explained to Elsa what had happened to the car. He also told her not to worry and instructed her to take Amy to Dorcas's apartment and wait for them there.

Torres detailed the situation to Luis and asked him to help him get his car back. Luis replied, "We'll get the car back from those suckers. That's all they are; they're a bunch of bastards. They know what they're doing, especially when they see a car with plates from another state. Don't worry, we'll get the car soon."

Luis was familiar with the traffic in Brooklyn and also knew some of the locations where the car had probably been taken. He had had similar experiences before with friends of his who had come to visit Dorcas and him and had their cars taken away and impounded at some distant depot.

When the two arrived at a depot, they checked around to see if any truck was hauling a vehicle in. The place had a high fence all around and the men had to look for the main entrance to the site. Luis parked his car close to a gate that seemed to be what they were looking for. They glanced around to see if there was anyone around they could ask for information or directions to the main office of the depot. Finally, after a couple of minutes, they saw a young man coming in their direction. He was carrying a tool box and walking up the alley very slowly. When he approached them, Luis asked, "Hey, buddy, have you seen a tow truck hauling a Studebaker with Hawaiian plates on it?"

The young man immediately replied, "Yes, it just came in. The tow truck will probably drop it in the last row down this alley." He pointed in the general direction in which he had seen the vehicle going.

The young man continued to walk toward a small building, saying, "Come with me. I'll take you to the office. There they can tell you what you have to do to get your car back." The young man thought rightly that the two men were looking for the car and that it belonged to the one dressed in military uniform, which was Torres.

Torres and Luis entered the small building right behind the young man, who told the attendant behind the desk, "Daniel, these two guys are looking for their car. It's the Studebaker that just came in. Will you help them?"

The attendant, who apparently was of Hispanic descent, told Luis and Torres, "Sirs, in order to get your car back, you must get a release order from a judge. Go to the Manhattan Civic Center, where the traffic courts are. There you'll have to pay a small fine and the tow charges. Bring the release order to me before 4:00 P.M. today; then you can get the car. That's the only way I can give it back to you, okay?"

He finished talking and walked away in the direction of a nearby coffee pot. Immediately Torres recognized that he was in for a long day and that he and Luis were going to be faced with a lot of hard times ahead.

The Manhattan courts were located in the same place, City Hall. Luis drove down Broadway toward the Civic Center. The trip was not without delays due to the traffic jams and the control lights all along the avenue, but they made it safely after almost thirty-five minutes of driving.

When they reached the Civic Center, Luis entered a municipal parking lot and they parked, then proceeded toward the court building. Both men entered through the front door and walked toward a desk located to the right of the main corridor. A man was seated behind the desk giving information to people standing in front of him.

Torres and Luis stood in line. When their turn came, Luis asked, "Sir, can you tell us how to get to the traffic court for impounded cars?"

The man replied, "There are a lot of rooms for traffic violations. What kind of violation did you commit?"

Luis answered, "My friend had his car impounded for illegal parking. He came from Hawaii yesterday to visit me and my wife. He didn't know about the alternate parking laws; there was no sign on the street."

The man told Luis and Torres to go to room 15 and explain things to the judge.

Torres and Luis walked down the aisle until they reached room 15. They opened the door and entered. A woman who seemed to be a court clerk asked what they were there for, and after Torres had briefly explained the situation, she pulled some papers from a nearby desk. Then she walked up to the judge, who was dressed in a black robe and was sitting behind the bench.

The judge, a white-haired, middle-aged man, immediately told the clerk he would hear the case after the woman informed him about Torres's plight. The clerk proceeded to call Torres and swear him in. There were no more questions or inquiries. The judge told Torres to approach the bench. He then proceeded to ask him how his car got impounded. Torres told the judge what he had told the others.

The judge told Torres, "Now I will give my decision. I cannot explain why you did not see the sign, and the law here is the same for everyone. The cars next to yours were probably impounded after they took yours. They can only take one car at a time."

The judge signed some papers and gave them to the clerk. The clerk called Torres and, after stamping the papers, gave them to him. She said, "Sergeant, go to the collector's cage outside of this room and to the left. He will tell you what to do. Give him these papers, which are already signed and stamped."

Torres thanked the judge and the clerk and he and Luis exited the room.

Once outside, both men proceeded to walk left until they reached the collector's booth. They again stood in line behind two more people who were also paying fines for traffic violations. When Torres reached the window and faced the collector, he handed him the papers he had been given. The collector immediately said, "Forty dollars, please. Fifteen for the hauling and twenty-five for the ticket."

The collector glanced at Torres and Luis outside the booth and, in a sarcastic tone, said, "That's the way it is. You pay or you don't get your car back." Looking at Torres, he added, "Let me tell you, Sarge, I was in the military and so was the judge who signed these papers. We served during World War II. We were in Panama and Trinidad. We didn't stay after the war. I didn't like the military life enough to stay in. Sarge, why do you stay in the army? You should get out."

Torres didn't say anything but wondered why the old man was giving him advice that he hadn't asked for. After all, he had not said a world to the man behind the booth, and he had certainly not asked him for the uncalled-for advice; he only wanted to get his car back.

Torres paid the forty dollars, but he was angered over the circumstances in which he had to practically get insulted for serving his country. Besides, he was trying to get back what properly belonged to him.

For a minute Torres wished that the United States was at war and that shots would be fired. *Let it happen in New York, but don't let anyone get hurt*, he thought. He wished that two shots would be fired and that they would hit the chairs where the judge and the collector were sitting! *Let it happen when both men are getting up from their chairs; just scare them enough to make them change their underwear!*

Luis and Torres left to pick up the car immediately after receiving the papers from the collector. On the way to the depot, they recalled some of the experiences they had had during the Korean War. The two had both served and had been decorated with Purple Hearts for wounds they'd received in action against the enemy. Luis and Torres had both been members of the 65th Infantry Regiment, an all-Puerto Rican unit that was attached to the 3rd Infantry Division, nicknamed "the Rock of the Marne."

Luis had not stayed in the military but instead had moved to New York City, where he'd met Dorcas and gotten married. He had gotten a job working at Bellevue Hospital in the food department. He liked his job and everyone respected and liked him.

Torres, in his conversations with Luis about the war, recalled an instance in which he had found himself and another member of the squad he commanded in a very difficult and dangerous situation. He remembered that the name of the other guy was Antonio and that he was an assistant gunner to the machine-gun squad Torres led.

It happened that Torres's unit was ordered to attack a hill known as Hill 153. It was Company I, 3rd Battalion, 65th Infantry Regiment. They were occupying positions along the 38th Parallel, just below the Imjin River.

Hill 153 was about 1,100 yards to the left of the infamous Pork Chop Hill, which, at the time, was occupied by the Chinese and North Koreans.

Almost every day Torres and the members of his squad could clearly see the enemy running around looking for cover

9

when the American forces delivered artillery barrages. Torres was also ordered to fire his squad's machine guns at the hill once in a while.

When Torres's company moved across the Imjin River to attack Hill 153, other elements or units of the battalion were supposed to give support and secure the withdrawal avenue or route back to friendly lines. Nobody had supported them or showed up, and the company commander gave the order to withdraw. Almost everyone took the same route in retreating that they had used going in.

The unit began to receive heavy artillery fire from the vicinity of Pork Chop Hill and also from other adjacent positions. Torres and Antonio found themselves separated from the unit and from the rest of the 3rd Platoon.

The two men crossed a very wide field that they had to test and probe for mines. Enemy artillery was landing all around them, and both men were slightly wounded. Torres got shrapnel in his left forearm, and Antonio was wounded in his left knee. It was the first experience in combat for both men, but they did not panic.

The moon was very bright and with its reflection on the ground you could see for at least five hundred yards. When both men had crossed the field, they climbed a small hill to get a better view of the area. At the top of the hill, they found an abandoned bunker where they sought refuge from the artillery.

The enemy quit shelling after almost thirty minutes of intense firing, and Torres and Antonio attended to their wounds. Antonio's kneecap was bleeding and swollen from the mortar shrapnel. Torres pulled the shrapnel from his arm himself, and bandaged Antonio's knee. It was August 7, 1952, and the Pammunjon's talks were going on for a cease-fire. Both men could see the lights of the reflectors far away, indicating that no one was to fire a weapon in that direction.

Torres and Antonio did not want to give away their positions, but they knew that they had to make it back to the friendly lines quickly. They decided that early the next day they would start walking down the hill in the general direction of their lines.

Just before daybreak they smelled a very foul odor and followed the smell to a trench that led to the bunker. The moon was still bright and gave enough light for them to see everything around them. Suddenly, right in front of them, they saw the most grotesque sight.

The smell was not from gas or any dead wild animal. It came from the bodies of five dead men in enemy uniforms. It appeared that they had been killed and had been lying there for at least five to ten days. The bodies were decomposed and repugnant; insects and worms were having a feast on them. Torres and Antonio wanted to get away immediately, but they knew that dead bodies did not harm anyone and they did not have to be afraid of them. They moved farther down the hill in the direction of another hill, which they recognized to be in friendly hands.

When they reached the foot of the hill, they moved across a field that they thought was mined like the others they had encountered. They moved slowly, constantly watching where they stepped. They started to climb the second hill and reached a barbed-wire area. They were sure they were close to a friendly outpost because they had passed through that area before. Suddenly, they received challenge from a sentinel, who was apparently on the alert and situated in a hidden position inside a bunker almost at the top of the hill. The sentinel gave them a different password than the one they had had before, and Torres, anticipating it, shouted in unison with Antonio, "We are Borinqueneers." "Somos Borinquenos." They hoped that the guard was not a trigger-happy fellow and would not start firing at them.

They yelled again, "Somos Borinquenos." It was the nickname that all the members of the 65th Regiment were known by in Korea. It was a name known to every Puerto Rican because Borinquen was the name the native Taino Indians called Puerto Rico when the island was discovered by the Spaniards on November 19, 1493. Therefore, Borinqueneer is analogous to Puerto Rican.

Torres also yelled the password used the day before the countersign; it was "Big Book." The sentinel then told them to advance and be recognized, and he walked down a short trench until he reached the edge of the barbed wire and could see them. The guard guided them carefully around and made them aware of the booby traps and flare devices attached to the wires that were blocking the path to the friendly positions.

The three men walked up the hill a short way to where the command bunker was located. There they separated, and the sentinel returned back to his original position. When Torres was about to enter the command bunker, he recognized a member of his squad, who was standing by the entrance to the bunker. He was a machine gunner called Rojas, who apparently had just arrived a few minutes before Antonio and Torres.

Inside the bunker there were some high-ranking officers who were making inquiries about the conduct of the attack the night before on Hill 153. Once of the officers asked Rojas, "Hey, soldier, how are things out there?"

Rojas immediately replied, "Look, man, I wish you could have been there and seen for yourself. It was like hell all over the place." Apparently Rojas did not recognize the officer who was asking him about the situation. It was Col. Ceasar Cordero, the regimental commander. The colonel had come to watch the conduct of the attack and wanted to know the results.

Torres smiled at Rojas and then told him to accompany Antonio to the aid station so that Antonio could get some first aid for his knee, while he followed to get treatment for his swollen forearm. It was not sore but Torres needed to be checked by a medic.

After being cared for, Torres said good-bye to Antonio, who was being taken to a rear-echelon hospital; then, together with Rojas, Torres went to join his unit. After both men made it back to the company, Torres found that he and Antonio had been reported missing in action. They also found that five men from the company had been badly wounded during the attack and that two had been killed. None of the men were from Torres's platoon.

By the time they reached the depot Torres had finished telling his story to Luis. After they got the car, the two drove back to Manhattan. Torres did not know the traffic as well as Luis, so he followed Luis all the way back. They arrived at the apartment, where Elsa and Amy were waiting for Torres. They were eager to depart.

They all had lunch together; then Torres loaded the suitcases in the trunk of the car. They left immediately, saying good-bye to Luis and Dorcas and thanking them for their hospitality and help.

2

Torres followed the directions Luis had given him to get across the George Washington Bridge and onto the New Jersey Turnpike. After two hours of driving, he left the turnpike at Exit 7 and then followed the signs to Fort Dix—his next duty station. He was going to be there for at least eighteen months before he would be shipped to an overseas area. That was the Army rule, except in cases of war.

Torres was a bit tired of running around New York and then driving for two hours to Fort Dix. He decided to take his family to the post guest house for the night. After securing a room, he rested for a couple of hours and then took his family to the post cafeteria for dinner.

Early the next day, after having breakfast at the cafeteria, Torres drove to the personnel center, where they told him to report to the replacement center located next to the parade ground known as Doughboy Field. There he met a sergeant by the name of Medina in charge of processing. He gave Torres orders that indicated he was being assigned to a training regiment.

It was the 4th Training Regiment, known as "the Pioneers," and it was located at the southwest end of the post. It had five training battalions, and Torres thought that he was going to be assigned to one of them. He liked to work with new recruits because he had done so from the time he was drafted until he'd graduated from basic training and qualified to attend a leadership school at Camp Tortuguero in Puerto Rico. He knew there were going to be long hours of work out in the field, but he accepted the challenge.

After receiving his orders from Sergeant Medina, Torres decided to go the billeting section of the post and apply for family quarters. The billeting clerk placed him on a waiting list. He could get quarters in about three months, which at the time was the minimum waiting period. Having filled in the necessary papers, and after securing a map to guide himself around the post, Torres took off for Regimental Headquarters.

At the Regimental Headquarters, where they knew of his imminent arrival, Torres was met by a sergeant major, who briefed him and welcomed him to the unit. He received orders that assigned him to the 3rd Training Battalion of the regiment. When he left Regimental Headquarters, Torres was told to report to Battalion Headquarters, where they would assign him to a training company.

At 1000 hours, Torres arrived at his new unit, where he was greeted by the first sergeant, who also knew he was coming. The first sergeant of the unit guided Torres to the company commander's office. The company commander was a young first lieutenant named Mahoney. He was a paratrooper and a Ranger graduate.

After the commanding officer had briefed him, while the first sergeant (whose last name was Pagnella) was standing nearby, Torres was offered enough assistance to make him feel sure he was going to have all the support he needed from the staff. He was told that his assignment as a cadre in the company was going to carry a dual responsibility. He would be a platoon sergeant; being the senior sergeant in grade, he would also be the field first sergeant. Torres was glad of confidence the commander and the first sergeant had shown in him. He knew he could do the job and gratefully accepted it.

After finishing his processing, where Torres met other members and was greeted by them, he was told by the first sergeant to take two days off and see to his family. He was also told that the company was in the field training and that he would be presented to the rest of the cadre when he returned. Torres went to see Elsa and told her about his assignment and how happy he felt about it. It was about 1200 hours, so Torres took his family for lunch. Then he decided to go to Philadelphia with them and try to get them an apartment there. He knew it was going to be hard to find an empty apartment around the post, and those that were available were neither cheap nor comfortable enough for what they were asking. Also, in Philadelphia they would see some of Elsa's relatives, who had offered them help if they needed it.

When they got to Philadelphia, they went straight to see a cousin named Eva and her mother, who was Elsa's oldest aunt; her name was Lucinda. The family were very happy to see them. They lived in an apartment located at 4th Street between Pine and South streets. They offered to help the Torreses find an apartment, even if it was only a temporary one. They also told them that Elsa and the child would be safe. They would check on Elsa and assist her in everything.

Torres was grateful and thanked them, especially an uncle nicknamed "Millan," whose proper name was Adrian. Torres thought of him as a father figure. Torres had known Millan since his own childhood, when he used to read the newspaper while Millan made cigars at a factory. Uncle Millan, besides being a cigarmaker by profession and a gambler, also worked as a baker in Philadelphia, a trade he had learned in Puerto Rico before he came to the United States after World War II.

Millan quickly found an apartment for Elsa and the child. He knew people and they liked him. The apartment was located just below and about three hundred yards from Eva's apartment. Roberto, Millan's oldest son, lived in his own apartment, which was in the same building where the Torreses' apartment was located.

16

The apartment had a bed and a crib big enough for Amy to sleep in. The landlord did not ask for any deposit or advance rent because he trusted Millan; he also met Torres, who seemed to the landlord responsible enough. He was sure he would be paid on time. The important thing was that the family felt secure and that everything was going well.

Torres would either have to drive to the post every morning or stay over sometimes at the base if he was going to perform his duties well. It was an hour's drive to the post and he had to take into consideration that sometimes he might run into accidents or traffic jams on the way. The best route was Route 38, which was a double-lane road. He would have to get up at 0400 if he was to be on time to get the trainees up and take reveille.

Reveille was scheduled for 0600 hours, unless the unit planned to go to marksmanship training; in which case they would most likely have to establish a bivouac in some wooded area close to the ranges and training areas they would use during the period. Sundays were the only days that reveille was scheduled to be at a later hour than 0600 and the trainee platoon sergeant helped the noncommissioned officer in charge of quarters make the muster call.

Torres reported the next day to the company and picked up his field equipment, asking the supply sergeant for some extra linens for his wife until his own household goods arrived from Hawaii. His property had been shipped about a week prior to the family's departure from the island.

Torres got to know every member of the unit, especially the ones who formed the company cadre team. He familiarized himself very well with the post training areas and learned the standard operating procedures of the training center by memory. There were long hours of work on every training day and even during the cycle breaks. Once a cycle finished, they had to get ready to start the other immediately.

Trainees were shipped to different posts throughout the

United States, and they could not keep them too long in the company's barracks because they had to make room for the next bunch. Torres, with the experience that he had, knew the procedure well. He had graduated from a leadership academy after finishing basic training and being promoted to corporal. By the time he had been in the military for four months, he was already a noncommissioned officer and had been assigned as assistant platoon sergeant at Camp Tortuguero in Puerto Rico. He'd advanced to become sergeant first class during the Korean War. He also attended the leadership academy of the 25th Division, from which he graduated with honors while he was in Hawaii. He also graduated from Troop Information School and the Chemical and Biological School at Fort Gulick, Panama.

The H Company supply sergeant, whose name was John Walton, became one of Torres's most trusted compeers by Torres's standards. The sergeant helped fill all the needs of the outfit at all times. From getting food to the soldiers in the field to securing transportation when needed, Sergeant Walton was always ready to do his part and more.

Walton was a very happy fellow, who always had a smile on his face and a friendly joke on his lips. For some people, the sergeant's attitude was hard to understand, as he had to put in long hours and always be on time. He kept the trainees, as well as the cadre, in high spirits every time he brought supplies to the field. The company trainees loved to help him unload and reload equipment onto the trucks.

On a rainy day early in November, the company was engaged in a marksmanship course on a newly opened range denominated Range 14, the transition range. Walton had gone to deliver supplies and the evening meal, as well as mail, to the company, which was in a bivouac area also numbered 14. When Walton arrived at the bivouac site, the heavy rain that had been falling had soaked the area and there were small puddles every-

18

where. Lightning started to strike all around them, and sometimes it seemed as though heavy artillery fire was falling everywhere. There were many pine trees around the bivouac area, and some of the lightning hit and split them in half.

Sergeant Walton was sitting on the wooden mailbox the trainees used to drop off their mail when they wrote their families and friends. He was waiting for the company to come back to the bivouac area and get supper. He was smiling and telling a joke to two trainees who had helped him unload equipment from the delivery truck. The two trainees were laughing when, suddenly, Walton stood up very rigid and fell on his face. A crack had been heard similar to that of a firecracker. A trainee grabbed his left leg and screamed. The other trainee could not even move.

Apparently lighting had struck a nearby tree and bounced off, hitting Walton and the trainee, who grabbed his leg. The flash of lightning had gone in between the two trainees and fully struck Walton.

When the rest of the people around heard the commotion and screams, all of the cadre arriving from the firing range at that time, along with the rest of the trainees, ran up to assist. The medic assigned to support the company gave CPR to Walton; then, not wasting any time, he placed him in an ambulance with other trainees. There was no sign of life in Walton's body, but there was hope.

Torres was at Battalion Headquarters getting some training schedules changed when he heard the news. He went immediately to the hospital and sat impatiently in the waiting area of the emergency room. He was hoping and praying that Walton would live and be alright.

Fifteen minutes later, the doctor came out and the look on his face was one of sympathy as well as exhaustion from his efforts in trying to save a life. He opened his lips and said, "I did my best. The sergeant was dead before he even stood from the box. He received the full impact of the flash. The trainees will be alright. I'm sorry," he concluded and then walked away with his head lowered.

Torres walked to the wall next to him; folding his right arm and leaning his face against it, he cried. He knew he had lost a friend.

It was a very sad week for the company and everyone who knew Walton. He was well known and liked by all those he'd met and talked to. He was married and had two kids; his family lived in Canada.

Torres wanted to accompany the body and tell the family about his feelings and everyone's concerns about Walton's death. He went to the funeral parlor located in the town of Mount Holly, bringing his own family to say good-bye to his friend. He had not been picked to accompany the body back since a detachment all ready for those duties was permanently assigned.

After the great loss, the mission of the unit continued and the trainees finished their training and were shipped to various posts for advanced training.

During the cycle break, Torres received his assigned quarters, and he moved his family from Philadelphia to the post. It was very convenient because now he did not have to travel as far to work, and he could get up later than 0400 as he had been doing.

For the next cycle, the company received 250 trainees. Except for two, they all came from New York, and the names seemed as though the men were mostly of Italian descent. There were only two trainees who were from Connecticut; one was named Sanders, the other Donovan.

At this time Torres was only a platoon sergeant because a master sergeant had arrived at the company and had taken over as field first sergeant. This was more convenient for Torres; he had more time to take care of the platoon on a full-time basis.

The two-story buildings were wooden and could accommodate about fifty trainees. Torres had fifty men in his platoon and also an assistant, who was a corporal; at one time he had ridden with the famous cyclists known as the Hell's Angels. His name was Peters, and he was very dependable.

Torres's responsibilities included the welfare of the men as well as teaching subjects like drill and ceremonies, bayonet, chemical warfare, and above all discipline, which was very much stressed by him. He took his men to breakfast, lunch, and supper every day.

On the second week of the cycle training, the two young trainees from Connecticut approached Torres before reveille call and formation. They looked like they were nervous and very uneasy. Donovan said to Torres, "Sergeant Torres, we want to talk to you. We have a problem, but we do not want anyone to know. We want to talk to you alone. Both of us have the same problem."

Torres replied, "Sure. You can talk to me. Let's go inside the orderly room. We'll talk inside the operation room."

The two trainees hesitated, and then Sanders said, "No, Sergeant, we want to talk inside the barracks. We have something to show you."

Torres said to the trainees, "Let me tell Corporal Peters to march the platoon for breakfast, and you two can come with me inside the barracks. You can talk to me in there."

The three men walked inside the building and Sergeant Torres called the barracks guard. "Young man, go and join the platoon for breakfast. After you finish, I'll send for you and you can come back to continue your duties as barracks guard."

The trainee replied, "Yes, Sergeant." He immediately left to join the platoon, which could be heard at a distance repeating the "Jodie's" cadence that Corporal Peters was giving them. The echo sounded, "Look at me. I am the best . . . Better than the rest. Am I right or wrong?"

The trainees repeated the cadence answering, "You are right. One, two, three, four; one, two, three, four."

Sanders and Donovan had come into the military under what was classified as the buddy system, and they had had double bunks assigned. They were part of the same squad, and they would also be assigned to advanced training once they finished basic. Donovan's bunk was the lower one and Sanders had the top bed. Their bunks were in the left middle of the barracks, facing the front door of the building.

Sanders walked over to the beds, Donovan following him. Torres immediately asked, "What is it you want to talk to me about?"

Donovan answered, "Sergeant, we are scared. Will you look at my bed under the pillow?"

Torres hesitated and said, "What's under there? A snake? What's the idea?"

But Donovan answered, "It's not a snake, Sergeant. There's nothing that will bite anyone, but will you please check it. What is under my pillow is also under Sanders's. They must have been put there this morning after we went to wash up because when we woke up this morning there was nothing there."

Torres, with a very determined mind, slowly lifted the pillow of Donovan's bed. Looking at what he'd found, he said, "It's only a piece of folded paper. What's wrong with it?"

Donovan replied, "Pick it up, Sergeant, and then check what is inside. It's bad."

Torres took the paper and, unfolding it, saw a drawing of a black hand like the one the Mafia use to threaten people. He immediately lifted up Sanders's and found there the same type of sketch.

Torres knew that the drawings were messages, messages that could mean the two trainees were going to be roughed up, possibly in what is called a pillow party, where the person's head is covered up while others jump on him and hit the individual all over his body.

The trainees were very nervous. They were right to be concerned; they knew the meaning of the drawings. Donovan said, "We don't have any enemies, but we are the only ones from Connecticut and with Irish names. We don't want to fight and then go to the stockade or maybe get killed. Help us, Sergeant. Will you help us, please? Somebody does not like us, and they are planning to beat us up. What can we do?"

Torres looked at both trainees and calmly said to them, "Listen, nobody is going to get beaten up. Nobody is going to fight. Nobody is going to get hurt or killed. Nobody. Trust me. If someone is going to beat anyone, I will do the beating, and I'm not going to do it. Don't worry. I will take care of the situation. Don't tell anyone about this, not even Corporal Peters. Do you understand? Nobody should know. Stay calm and I will handle this."

Torres took both papers and, folding them together, he placed them inside the upper left pocket of his fatigue jacket. Immediately he said to Donovan and Sanders, "Both of you, go now and join the platoon at the mess hall. Go and eat breakfast. Don't waste time. Also, tell Corporal Peters to send the barracks guard back here. I'll be waiting until he comes back on duty."

The trainees exited the front door and double-timed it back to the platoon, perhaps thinking that Sergeant Torres would try to get a transfer for them to another unit as a precaution, a unit where nobody would threaten them and they would also be safe.

Torres inspected the barracks and minutes later the appointed barracks guard reported back to duty. Torres said to him, "Check the latrines on both floors and lock the side door. We don't want anyone coming into the barracks and stealing equipment or personal belongings. Before you go to lunch, be sure you lock the front door also. Keep your eyes open and do a good job."

The trainee nodded in an affirmative way, indicating that the orders he had received were understood. He immediately replied, "Yes, Sergeant. I will."

Torres walked out the front door of the barracks and hastened to join the platoon, which had already finished breakfast and been aligned in the proximity of the mess hall by Corporal Peters. Corporal Peters asked Torres, "Is everything alright, Sergeant?"

"Yes," replied Torres. "There's no problem. Let's move the platoon for police call and then we can join the rest of the company at the company assembly area. We have the introduction to bayonet training the first four hours this morning."

After the area had been policed properly and the platoon was assembled, the other three platoons were also ready and waiting for orders. A training officer by the name of Ford gave the orders to Sergeant Torres to move the company to the training site.

Torres placed himself at a proper distance where he could be heard by the other platoon sergeants and assistants as well as by the trainees. Immediately he called the company, "Companeeey."

The platoon sergeants in unison relayed the command and sounded off to each platoon, "Platooon."

Torres, after allowing enough time for the men to be on the alert for the next command, said, "Attention. Right face. Right shoulder arms. Forward, march." He took enough time to make sure that all preliminary commands were properly understood and had been repeated by each platoon commander; then he started to count cadence. To inspire the trainees, he also used the Jodie's cadence. He reflected on the recent experience, and to inspire confidence in Donovan and Sanders, he said, "Look at me. I am the best. Better than the rest. I am not scared. You are a freak. You are no good. We'll get you. You are a snook. Am I right or wrong?"

The company, in unison, repeated each line and then counted cadence, "One, two, three, four . . . one, two, three, four."

Torres continued, "I am brave. You are a coward. I know you. You are a dodoo. Am I right or wrong?"

Once again the unit repeated the lyrics and, at the command "Sound off," they counted the cadence as before.

The day went by without incident, except for the usual mild headaches and sweating due to the warm weather and the training conditions. A break was allowed as usual every hour; these were scheduled to last ten minutes each and sometimes evoked the old military saying, "Take ten minutes' break. Expect five. Have none." At least it seemed that way as the time flew by. For a headache, the order was to take two aspirins and a cup of water and then join the platoon. For fatigue, take one salt tablet with a cup of water. One more day of training and wait for the next.

The next day just before breakfast, two more trainees came to see Sergeant Torres. They wanted to tell him they had found drawings of a black hand under their pillows. These were identical to the drawings Donovan and Sanders had found. They were given to Torres, who immediately gave the trainees the same advice he'd given Sanders and Donovan. He said, "I'll take care of this. Don't worry. Don't say anything to anyone."

The next day, which was a Friday, the situation repeated itself. This time it happened to three other trainees. Torres's advice was the same as before. It seemed that everyone in the platoon was getting the same drawing under their pillows and the mystery remained. Everyone was looking suspiciously at each other, and they took their friendships as well as their threats very seriously. Torres gave everyone the same advice. By the end of the third week, everyone in the platoon had found a sketch of a black hand under their pillow. Nobody had any idea where they were coming from or who the culprit was that was trying to intimidate them. After all, Donovan and Sanders were the first to get one and they had not come to any harm yet.

Suddenly, after the end of the third week of training and at the beginning of the fourth, a different attitude was noted among platoon members. They had begun to look after each other, almost like members of a brotherhood society. They had begun to work as a team and were only concerned with becoming the best platoon. They encouraged each other, and they never quit at anything. The mood stayed the same through the remaining weeks of training until graduation time.

Basic training was over and all what remained was to march to Fort Dix's Doughboy Field and parade in front of their loved ones, who had come from all over New England and New York to watch and congratulate them.

Torres's platoon stood proudly, wearing well-earned insignias and badges. Their stiff, starched uniforms and shiny helmets were indications of their spirit and pride. They had learned team work and camaraderie. Torres advised them to be truthful to themselves and said, "Remember, know yourself and help each other wherever you may go. Be proud and respect each other. You may have to go into combat sometime and dependability will be the key there to success and survival."

Torres marched in front and to the left of the right row of the platoon, while Corporal Peters was at the right rear. The trainee platoon sergeant was to the right and in front, in line with Torres. Everyone marched to the cadence of the music of the Fort Dix Army Band. After the ceremony was over, and before being dismissed by Torres, they threw their hats up in the air and yelled, "Hip, hip, hooray," three consecutive times. They had leaves to enjoy before reporting to their new stations.

What about the mysterious black hands? Who was the culprit? Torres never bothered to find out who was trying to intimidate Donovan and Sanders, but he surely knew who had placed the hands under the other pillows. It is called reverse psychology. He had placed the hands there himself and had never told anyone. He did not care who had placed the drawings under Donovan's and Sanders's pillows. His mission had been accomplished and another group of young men was already waiting at the replacement station. He was ready to go once more after a short break in the cycle.

3

The month of October arrived and Torres received orders to report to Fort Devens, Massachusetts. They were temporary orders and many other NCOs around the post were alerted also. The orders specified that they must report to Fort Devens and join the 2nd Infantry Brigade.

The brigade was on alert to be deployed to Lebanon, in the Middle East, if necessary. There was a civil war going on there, and already marine units had been deployed in the immediate area. Permanent orders of assignment could be cut any time, if needed. Torres's family were to remain at Fort Dix, and they already had assigned quarters at Kennedy Courts Family Housing area. They were going to be safe, and Elsa's sister Irma was with them. Hospital care, post exchange, commissary, bus services, and military patrolling around the dependents' areas were available. Torres did not worry about his family's safety. They were well taken care of. There were also good neighbors living in the area and some even spoke Spanish. Some were from Hawaii, and Torres's wife knew them.

Torres departed for his temporary duty assignment at Fort Devens. He drove his old Studebaker from Fort Dix to Massachusetts without any problems and no delays. It took eleven hours to get there. He immediately reported to the personnel center, where he received orders to join Company C of the 60th Infantry Regiment. The regiment was one of two that composed the 2nd Brigade. The other regiment was the 4th Infantry Regiment. The 2nd Brigade was the only active combat brigade in the army at the time. The brigade's insignia was a patch with two bayonets pointing in opposite directions. One bayonet was blue with a white background; the other was white with a blue background. The unit had an excellent record as a combat unit.

Torres was processed in and given orders to report to Company C, 60th Infantry. Vaccinations and personal wills were completed the first day, and Torres immediately reported to his unit, where he was assigned to be a squad leader with a dual assignment as assistant platoon sergeant of the 1st Platoon.

The regiment was engaged in a rigorous training program during the months of October and November. The conflict in Lebanon did not seem to get any worse. It was getting very cold all over New England and very often snow-covered roads had to be traveled to engage in particular phases of training. Camp Edwards and Camp Drum were distant areas where the regiment trained. Every fifteen days Torres traveled to Fort Dix on the weekends to check on his family and inquire as to their needs and welfare. He telephoned on the weekends if he could not see them.

Torres was assigned to be part of a ceremonial burial detail that very often had to travel to nearby communities from the post. Traveling sometimes to other adjacent states like Maine, Vermont, or Connecticut, and close to the Canadian border was very difficult due to weather conditions and the treacherous roads, often covered by snow and ice.

Some members of the group, like Torres, were on temporary duty orders and wished to receive orders for Lebanon, where they could become another Lawrence of Arabia. They spent the time talking about how long it would take to brush a camel if they were given one.

The burial detail participated in ceremonies almost every weekday and it became routine to them. They traveled to Lowell, Ayer, Shirley, Worchester, and Boston. They witnessed much grief and suffering, but it was their duty and they felt honored to be the ones rendering tribute to the deceased veterans and servicemen who had proudly served their country. There were also instances where some oddities and peculiar behavior were observed among relatives of the deceased.

On one occasion, the detail traveled to a nearby community to render honors to a First World War veteran. He was about eighty years old when he died. He had also been remarried for a short period of time. At the end of the ceremony at the burial site, the officer in charge started to look for the surviving widow to present her with the American flag. He couldn't find her anywhere. After checking around, he finally found her in the limousine that had carried her to the cemetery. The widow was a very petite young lady about twenty-five years old. Very sophisticated, frivolous, and charming. She was accompanied by a young man about her own age. She was kissing and hugging him frenziedly; she was certainly not mourning her deceased husband.

The officer could not believe what he was seeing and neither could some of the detail members. The funeral director said, "Everything here is finished. Let's go have a cup of coffee. I invite all of you."

The group banded together and walked to the vehicles that were waiting nearby. In a convoy, they followed the director, who had told the lady and the young man that they should rent a room; he had to go and get ready for the next customer.

The vehicles stopped by the side of the main street of town and all the men proceeded to follow the director inside the cafeteria. They sat around taking refreshments and coffee. Then the funeral director started to talk about the previous incident. He said, "You guys haven't seen anything yet. Listen, I buried a man last year who was older than the one we just buried. His widow was about thirty years old and her mother was about fifty. After the old man was buried, neither woman was in sight. Then I heard some moans and groans coming from my limousine, the same one I'm driving today. I walked over to check out what was going on, thinking that maybe the grief had been too much for the widow and that maybe her mother had taken her away to console her and they had gotten in the car. The crying was loud and sounded desperate. When I reached the limousine—what a sight! I couldn't believe it, but there it was. The mother saw me, but she did not get excited or anything. She was in the back seat and her daughter was in the middle seat; each of them was with a young man. They looked like twins. Both couples were almost naked. Guess what the mother said to me. 'Honey, never mind us; we'll give you a big tip. Motels are quite expensive, and besides, you have air conditioning here. Don't mind us, please. Let us finish.' It was truly an orgy." When he concluded his story, everyone laughed.

The director continued to talk and said, "I could tell you all kinds of stories. In this business you see a lot of things, but few people really grieving or feelings of sympathy."

"Well, you have to be diplomatic and understand your business," Torres said.

"You bet I do. You may have to come this way sometime. There are many old veterans living in this area, and I do good business, believe me," the director said.

The friendly talk continued for about fifteen minutes; then the director said, "If you need anything, just ask for it. Everything is paid for."

One member of the squad said, "Hey, sir. Give me a call if any of those young widows want to be consoled. I'll be here right away. I won't mind."

The director glanced over in his direction and smiled while saying, "Good-bye, fellows. Take care of yourselves. Thanks for the services; you were great. If you come to honor me when I die because I'm a veteran, don't worry about consoling my wife; she's old and only likes caretakers. I'm glad I'm the only one around here and she doesn't know how to drive." Then he left.

The last burial ceremony was at a small town south of the city of Worcester. It was scheduled for 1000 hours, December 18th, and Torres had requested a leave of absence to start on the 20th of December. When the detail arrived at the burial site about 0930 hours, the deceased veteran had already been buried two hours earlier. Taps and the firing salvo were done beside the grave. The American flag was presented to the funeral director, who in turn promised to give it to the relatives of the deceased.

Christmas was due to arrive and Torres wanted to spend it with his family. His fifteen-day leave request was approved by the company commander and Torres left Fort Devens at 0730 hours on the 20th of December. Driving his old Studebaker, he exited Fort Devens en route to see his loved ones and hoping to share the coming holidays with Elsa and Amy, as well as Irma, who was still living with them at their Fort Dix quarters.

Driving down Route 2, Torres planned only to stop for gas and maybe an occasional cup of coffee to keep him awake if needed. He wanted to get home by at least 1900 hours. He didn't want to take any chances and drive over the speed limit. His car was running well, and he was not a risk taker. It was better to be little late than not to get there at all. Exiting Route 2, he reached Merritt Parkway in Connecticut and crossed the George Washington Bridge in New York at 1700 hours. He knew he would be home in about two more hours.

Torres tuned his car radio to the Hispanic station WADO in New York and thought about the Colon family. He did not have time to sit at their apartment, but he thought that it could be done around Christmas and he could bring all the family, as Elsa wanted. While listening to some Spanish Christmas carols, he entered the New Jersey Turnpike.

At 1850 hours, he left the pike at Exit 7 and turned onto Route 206, then turned to Route 68, the road that led to Fort Dix.

Twenty minutes later, Torres arrived at the apartment, where his family was watching a musical program on television. Elsa happily greeted him, and Amy and Irma came over to embrace him. It was already 1925 hours. Elsa offered him a cup of coffee; she knew he loved the flavor and taste. He said, "I'm tired. I'll eat something later, just give me coffee for now."

Suddenly a knock was heard at the door, just as Torres was taking his first sip of coffee. Torres thought that maybe the neighbors knew of his arrival and had come over to say hello. He stood up and walked to the door. Before opening it, he peeped through the peephole, after putting on the front-porch light. He saw the figure of a young man with a tablet in his left hand and a pencil in his right. He thought that perhaps it was someone soliciting for charitable organizations or looking for a newspaper subscription.

He opened the door slowly and the young man asked, "Are you Sergeant Torres?"

"Yes, I am," Torres replied.

"I have a telegram for you," the young man said. He handed the envelope to Torres and then said, "Have to deliver more telegrams around here. Will you sign here, please?" He handed the tablet and pen to Torres. Torres immediately signed and handed the tablet and pen back to the messenger. Then he called Elsa and said, "Is anyone sick back home? I hope it's not bad news. Do you know anything? Have they called you?" Torres was referring to Elsa's family, or maybe his own, back in Puerto Rico.

He opened the envelope after closing the front door and proceeded to read the message: "Dear Sergeant Torres, this telegram is to inform you that your leave is canceled. You must return immediately to your TDY unit at Fort Devens no later than 1700 hours on the 21st of December. Your TDY status will be terminated, and after you clear the post, you will proceed to report back to your permanent unit of assignment at Fort Dix, New Jersey."

Torres did not even glance at the signature of the sender but immediately called Elsa and said, "Honey, I have to go back to Fort Devens right now."

Elsa, not knowing what was going on, asked, "Why?"

"My TDY is finished and I'm not going to give them a chance to change their minds. I must leave right away. I can be back tomorrow evening. I'll drink my coffee on the way."

Torres checked his uniform, kissed Elsa and Amy, embraced Irma, then said, "For sure I will be here tomorrow. Don't worry. I'll drive back carefully. I'll get there by the morning. I'm very happy. Wait for me."

Torres walked out the front door in the direction of his parked car. Opening the driver's side, he stepped in, closed it, and put on his seat belt.

While watching from the porch, Elsa said to Irma and Amy, "I hope he does not feel sleepy and may the Good Lord watch over him. I don't know why he doesn't wait until tomorrow and leave early. It's a little bit crazy. Anyway, I think he'll make it. I know him well. We'll pray for his safety."

Elsa knew that her husband was excited and was not about to wait after he received the telegram. She watched him drive away in his car, waving his left arm in a sign of good-bye. His car disappeared around a curve.

Torres drove all night, stopping only once in a while to get his car gassed up at a station. He sometimes went to a restroom and washed his face. He also bought some coffee from some machines.

Torres arrived at Fort Devens at 0750 hours. He checked in at the gate and immediately proceeded up the road to the company location. After parking his car, he walked up to the orderly room and entered the office. He said to the company clerk, "I'm Sergeant Torres. I received a telegram, and I want to get my clearance papers right now, if possible."

The clerk nodded his head in the affirmative and said, "I have them right in my box."

He checked the out correspondence box. After finding

them, he said, "Here they are. Just sign wherever there's an X. I'll take care of the rest. Bring them back after you finish turning in your equipment at the supply room. Clear it last."

Torres said, "You bet. I'll do it as quickly as I can; I want to get out of here. No offense, this is a good post, but I would rather be closer to my family at Fort Dix." Torres thought maybe the clerk believed what he said, but actually he didn't want to be stationed there.

Torres went quickly to his car and, driving to the place already marked, he proceeded to clear the post.

By 2100 hours Torres had completed all that was needed to clear the company supply, after taking his bedding and combat gear from his sleeping room. He walked to the supply room, and the supply sergeant signed the papers, after Torres had accounted for all his equipment and turned it in.

He returned to the orderly room and handed his clearance papers to the company clerk. After receiving the papers, the clerk walked into the company commander's office to collect his signature. He walked out and handed Torres a copy of the clearance papers. He said, "You must sign the sign-out book before you go. Good luck and take care of yourself, Sarge. Maybe I'll see you sometime in the future."

Torres said "Well, I hope to see you, but not here. Thanks to all of you. I wish you the best. Have a Merry Christmas and a Happy New Year."

Torres left the office. He wanted to say good-bye to some of his platoon companions and wish them well. He walked into the barracks and shook hands with some of the guys. He said, "I'll be at Fort Dix. If you ever get there, look me up. Good luck to all of you." Then he walked away and got into his car.

He thought that the hardest part had been done. Now he could take his time and drive back. For the third time, he started down the same road he'd traveled twice in the last two days. He left Fort Devens at 1000 hours, crossed the George Washington

Bridge at 1900 hours, and exited the New Jersey Turnpike at 2000 hours. Finally, at 2135 hours, he arrived home, where his family was surprised when he walked through the front door and said, "I'm back."

Torres walked up the stairs to the second floor, unbuttoned his khaki shirt, and sat on the bed. He took off his shoes. For the first time he felt exhausted. He threw himself back, rolled over, and closed his eyes.

At 1000 hours the next day, December 22nd, Elsa was cooking him breakfast. Torres stepped into the shower and for the first time realized that he had completed an endurance drive of almost thirty-eight hours with minimal stopping. He walked downstairs, kissed his wife, gave Irma a hug, and kissed Amy, who was watching one of her favorite cartoons on television.

Elsa said, "Boy, are you something. I hope you never have to do that again. It's very dangerous to drive so much without resting, but I'm glad you're back with us. I couldn't sleep the night you left."

Torres replied, "It's okay; I feel great. I'll call the company very shortly and ask them for a leave. In fact, I'll do it now."

Torres departed after finishing his late breakfast. Fifteen minutes later he arrived at the company area, where he was greeted by some old friends, who were also happy to see him. He was told by the first sergeant that his job was waiting for him and he would be in charge only of the 1st Platoon because a master sergeant had arrived recently at the unit. He, being the highest ranking noncommissioned officer, was assigned as field first sergeant.

For Torres it was more convenient because he could now put all his time to concentrating on training his platoon. Corporal Peters would still be his assistant.

4

Torres received his leave orders and, after signing out, immediately went home where, together with Elsa, they started to make plans for Christmas. They planned to visit relatives and shop. Sooner or later he might have to depart for another overseas assignment and perhaps his family would not be able to go with him.

A year later, in the early part of December, Torres arrived at the apartment and called Elsa. He said, "Honey, I have orders to go to Korea. I'll have to be there for a year. There's no war on there now. You can't go with me, but I'll make sure you and Amy are taken care of. You can stay at an apartment in Fort Buchanan in Puerto Rico, or I can get an apartment around here. It's up to you."

Elsa replied, "Don't worry. We can stay with Mother at her apartment. She has room for us, and she'll gladly accept us. She's already told me that if you have to go somewhere and we can't go along, we can stay with her."

Torres's orders indicated that he had to report to his unit in Korea not later than the 27th of December, and that he had to leave Fort Dix on the 22nd. He made quick arrangements to clear the post and take his family to Puerto Rico. He could also stay there and visit his wife's family as well as his own. He would have at least ten days and then he had to report back to Fort Dix and pick up his plane tickets for Korea. He would be traveling on a commercial airline to Seoul.

Torres left Puerto Rico on the 22nd of December and, after securing his traveling tickets and an overnight stay at the replacement station at Fort Dix, he boarded a limousine for the international airport at Philadelphia. His flight was scheduled to leave for San Francisco at 2100 hours, and it would be arriving during the early hours on Christmas Eve.

Torres thought that maybe the plane would make a stop in Honolulu and he could probably see some of the friends he had known when he was at Schofield Barracks. Elsa and he had lived in a nearby town called Wahiawa when Amy was just a baby. He wanted to send a greeting card home with a few lines telling them he was alright and missed them.

The plane departed two hours later after refueling at San Francisco Airport. It was not scheduled to stop at Honolulu. The next refueling stop was going to be at the island of Wake in the middle of the Pacific. Aboard the aircraft were members of other branches of the armed services besides the U.S. Army. The plane was full and there were no empty seats left.

It was 1400 hours when suddenly the pilot said, "Merry Christmas, everyone. We've just crossed the International Dateline and it is the 25th of December."

The stewardesses served snacks and greeted everyone aboard. Back home it was not even noontime.

Not long after, the plane landed at Wake Island, where Santa Claus was waiting for the passengers to get out of the plane while the craft was being refueled. It was about 90 degrees above zero, and it seemed to be the right spot for Santa if he wanted to drop weight. Two hours later the plane continued its flight to Japan, where the passengers would be boarding other flights to Korea.

Torres arrived in Korea and the time seemed to pass by very quickly. Ten months later he received orders to fill out papers and request his station of preference in the United States. He completed his request and chose his favorite place, Fort Dix. As a second choice he selected Puerto Rico, although he knew that his chances to serve there were very slim. As a third choice he clearly wrote, "Anywhere except Fort Devens."

Torres received his orders in the early part of December that he was to leave Korea on the 21st of the month. His stateside assignment read: 60th Infantry Regiment, 2nd Brigade, Fort Devens, Massachusetts.

He arrived at the post and immediately got a short discharge. He reenlisted with a guarantee that he would be once more reassigned to Fort Dix, New Jersey.

Together the Torres family arrived at Fort Dix after Torres had spent his leave at Puerto Rico. His assignment at Fort Dix this time was to be a different mission; he was not to work with basic training as before. He was going to be field first sergeant in an advanced training unit that had the mission of training clerks for supply administrative positions.

The men going through training received four to eight weeks of instruction in supply procedures. After they graduated, some were assigned to different units in the United States and overseas.

There was a special mission that the trainees sometimes had to perform. It happened that next to the sleeping quarters there was a special barracks that had to be guarded twenty-four hours a day. The occupants were men who had been sent from other units around the post and from nearby military installations. They were classified as homosexuals, and they were due to be processed out of the service. Sometimes there were more than twenty in the barracks.

Although sometimes it seemed there were parties in the barracks, everything looked normal and quiet. The charge of quarters of Company D, the company Torres was assigned to, had the responsibility of checking the building and putting the lights off at 2200 hours every night. Torres accompanied him when he made his rounds.

As Torres walked in, accompanied by the charge of quarters, he knew they were going to hear the same phrases as they walked by the bunks. "Will you stay for a while after you put the lights out?" "Do you want to get warm?" "Please stay for ten minutes." As usual, the voices were low and tender. Some of the guys making the remarks had their heads covered with blankets. Torres replied, "Shut up and go to sleep; you need the rest."

In unison, voices could be heard from everywhere, "Will you tuck me in, Sarge. Please come over and tuck me in."

Once more Torres shouted, "Shut up and go to sleep, you sweethearts."

But as he and the charge of quarters were about to walk out the door, almost from every bunk the sound of voices in unison could be heard, "Good night, honey. Good night, Sarge."

When both men were out the door, Torres glanced toward the charge of quarters and said, "The 'Good night, honey' was for you and the 'Good night, Sarge' was for me. My advice to you is not to ever walk in there by yourself." Both men laughed as they continued to walk in the general direction of the orderly room.

It was early summer when Torres received instructions from the first sergeant to report to Battalion Headquarters and be briefed in relation to a special assignment. Torres had been selected, along with seven more noncommissioned and six commissioned officers. Torres did not know what it was about, but there were rumors of some men going on per-diem pay, or that subsistence allowance was to be given to the volunteers. The money was to include an initial allowance of $400 to buy civilian clothes and other immediate necessities.

When Torres reported to Battalion Headquarters, he was

redirected to report to a nearby conference room. All fourteen men were seated. Torres knew some of them and greeted one who was seated to his right in the front row. He was an old friend named Domingo Rodriguez. Both men had served together with the 14th Infantry Regiment while Torres was stationed at Schofield Barracks in Hawaii.

"Hello, Rod," Torres said. "I wonder what this is all about. I expect we'll find out very soon."

"Me too," Rodriguez said. "I already have an idea and if it's suitable, I'll go—whatever it is."

Some of the men present were dressed in civilian clothes and had badges identifying them as members of the State Department.

It was 0800 hours and a captain, identifying himself immediately, said, "Good morning, men. I am Captain Blair, the assistant S-3 for field operations. You have been selected to attend briefings for three days, and I must remind you that everything you hear is strictly confidential. If you discuss anything except the personal desire to accept the assignment, which will be discussed and presented to you by the briefers, you will be subject to receive the appropriate punishment under the Military Code of Justice. You can discuss with your immediate relative whether or not to accept the job, but no other information may be given out under any circumstances.

"You must be present at all briefings and on time. The staff presenting the information has come from the Department of the Army, and they are considered experts in these matters. You can ask any questions if you so desire."

The captain concluded his presentation and immediately a gentlemen proceeded to start his briefing. "Men, the reason you have been summoned here is to receive information about the situation in Southeast Asia, mainly in South Vietnam. As you know, American forces have been deployed as advisors and observers and the situation seems to be very unstable. More assistance is needed, and we hope that we will not have to send ground forces or any other type of help, besides the advisory and observing types. North Vietnam has moved some Army forces across the 17th Parallel, and guerrilla forces have intensified their campaigns in the south." The presenter continued his rhetoric about the general situation, and one after the other the Department of the Army personnel continued the briefings.

After two long days of receiving information, on the afternoon of the third day one of the presenters announced the purpose of the meeting. "All of you have been in here for the last three days and by now you probably know the reason for your having been chosen to attend this conference. Everything in here is strictly confidential, and now it is up to you whether you want to volunteer to go to South Vietnam as an observer or advisor or not. You must submit your answer and be ready for more training. You will be granted enough time to talk to dependents. You have forty-eight hours to make your decision and fill in the proper paperwork," he concluded.

Sergeant Rodriguez looked at Torres and said, "I want to go. How about you, Torres?"

"Well, I'll think it over. I don't think I'll be leaving my family so soon. I'll have to check with my wife, but I don't think I'll go for now. The army is developing a new program for preparing drill sergeants, and I think I'd like to be one. You go first and take care of yourself out there. I may be there later. Maybe I'll be sent somewhere in the future where I can take my family with me, like Hawaii. Or I may get orders for Europe next year." Torres shook hands with Rodriguez and once more wished him good luck.

It was September 1962, and Torres received orders for Germany and became a member of the same unit he had served in during the Korean War. The 3rd Infantry Division had been stationed in Europe, and Torres was assigned to the 30th Infantry

Regiment. Torres made the trip without his family, who were to join him at a later date when quarters would be available for them.

Elsa arrived with Amy a month later. A year later Kennedy was assassinated and forty days later a new baby girl had been born into the Torres family. Her name was Sigrid.

The year was 1965 when Torres applied to be admitted to the drill sergeant program, once he'd rotated back to the United States. He was accepted and attended the Second Army Drill Sergeant's School, located at Fort Knox, Kentucky. His family was with him; Amy was already in the fourth grade.

Torres graduated as drill sergeant and was assigned to Company C of the 17th Battalion at the Armor Center. He received various Certificates of Achievement and Letters of Commendation, including one from the chief of staff of the U.S. Army, accompanied with seven endorsements.

5

The Vietnam buildup of American forces was in full swing almost right after the Gulf of Tonkin incident in August 1964. The U.S. Congress passed the Gulf of Tonkin Resolution, and Marine forces landed at the coastal town of Da Nang. By the end of the year 1965, the American forces were around two hundred thousand, which included ground combat forces and many advisory units assisting the Vietnamese forces and other paramilitary units.

In June 1967, Torres received orders to report on July 30th to Fort Bragg, North Carolina, and undergo a special training in which he would be instructed as an advisor to assist the Vietnamese paramilitary and regular army forces. He had to report to the Special Warfare School, which was under control of the Special Forces Command. He would undergo four weeks of preparation, which would include some basic Vietnamese language training. It also included training in enemy combat-support weapons, tactics, deployment, and some cultural background as to the local food, clothing, religions, and, above all, the geographical features of the countryside. Along with Torres were members of all the branches of the armed forces, including commissioned officers. The ranks of the enlisted personnel were staff sergeants to sergeant majors from the army, marines, and air force. Petty officers from the navy and coast guard were also there.

The school, situated at a convenient location, had a building honoring the late president John F. Kennedy. It was called the John F. Kennedy Center.

The men undergoing training and those in the process of starting training were divided into groups of nine to twelve men, squad size; these were assigned to classes designated as sections, with each section having over fifty men. The sections were identified as Section A and Section B. Torres was attached to Section A, along with fifty-four other noncommissioned officers from all branches of the services.

When Torres arrived, he was told that the training would last from July 31st to September 8th. The men were bunked by squads in barracks similar to those at Fort Dix, which had double bunk beds. Torres was assigned a lower bunk on the top floor. A sergeant first class, also a member of the army, was assigned to sleep in the top bunk; his name was Hicks.

Torres and Hicks became very good friends. Hicks was a huge, muscular fellow who weighed about 280 pounds and was over six feet tall. He came from Fort Ord, California. He was very vociferous and arrogant but a very funny guy at times. Many times Torres and Hicks went to a nearby club to drink a cold beer after training was over for the day. They talked about their experiences. From their conversation it seemed as if they had known each other for a long time. At the club they enjoyed the Sandy Sadler tunes about the Green Berets and the other songs referring to the Vietnam War. Both men were attached to the same squad. They were also hoping that they could get assigned to the same team or advisory unit.

The course had been designated MATA Senior Noncommissioned Officer Courts 1-68. The initials MATA stood for military assistance training advisor. Advisory groups were already dispersed throughout all of South Vietnam, many of them from the Special Forces military contingency. They were assigned under the control of corps commanders and subsequently were designated numbers from 1st to 4th Corps.

The Special Warfare School had Vietnamese teachers instructing them in the language, customs, and traditions of the varied Vietnamese cultures. Torres's teacher was named Ba Than, which means Mrs. Than. She was a good teacher, and the group liked her very much.

The main purpose of the training, stressed by the instructors at all times, was the emphasis on Vietnamizing the war so that the Vietnamese Army could take over the responsibilities of all military operations. Their duties would include fighting, defense, and also winning the hearts and minds of the civilian population of South Vietnam.

For Torres, picking up basic Vietnamese was not much trouble because the alphabet was the same as Spanish and almost all the pronunciations were the same. Accents over words were used, which simplified Vietnamese. The word *nhieu* in front of a singular name for anything made the word plural. Mrs. Than was married and the word *ba* meant married. If the word *nhieu* was placed in front of *ba*, it meant married women (*nhieu ba*).

Training at Fort Bragg was intense and well organized. It included recognition of enemy and friendly forces, civilian organizations, weapons used by the enemy, and assembly and disassembly of the same. The enemy physically looked the same as the forces the advisors would be working with and the students were told that sometimes the units they might be advising would have enemy sympathizers. They must have their eyes open when engaged in combat situations.

The five weeks of training came to an end, and a graduation ceremony was held under the roof of the John F. Kennedy Center. There were some outside guests, including families of some of the graduates. Diplomas were presented to each student. Right after, the men picked up their leave orders. They were given plane tickets to report to Oakland Army Base, located in Oakland, California. There they would receive subsequent orders indicating their departure date for Vietnam.

Torres and Hicks had already taken their leaves, and they would be traveling together. They would depart on a military C130 plane, along with others going the same way.

Torres had taken his family to Puerto Rico prior to reporting to school. He was happy that his family was secure at Fort Buchanan and would be accommodated there for the year he was going to be away. The girls could attend schools nearby, and Elsa could shop at the post exchange and the commissary. Relatives could visit them and keep them company. Health clinics and transportation services were also available. For their two poodles, a veterinarian clinic was also nearby.

Hicks and Torres boarded the military aircraft along with the other men and departed en route to Oakland International Airport. Hicks, being a very verbal individual, began to make remarks about the trip and his feelings. He was not aggressive but was a very happy fellow in nature. He had been married for fifteen years and had two boys. One was eight and the other twelve.

"Hey, Torres. When I get to Nam I'm going to finish that war. It will only take me five to seven days. They shouldn't send you over there. I can handle it myself."

Torres answered, "You'd better take care of yourself and remember that somebody is waiting for you at home."

Hicks continued, "You know, it seems to me that if you take a Vietnamese and place it next to a monkey and then shave the monkey, you'd never notice the difference."

Torres replied, "Agh, Hicks. That's not nice. Shut up, you baboon."

Hicks said, "Let me tell you. Put me next to a gorilla and just by my looks I could conquer the world. I'm strong and huge. After all, we're supposed to come from apes, according to Darwin. I believe in the Lord, but I also think that Darwin's theory is right. I said I'll end that war in Nam when I get there. You'll see."

The plane landed at Oakland International, and the men were instructed to secure their baggage, which had been placed at the end of the plane. A military bus was waiting to pick them up and transport them to the base. The bus driver assisted them in loading their equipment into the bus' lower side compartments, and everyone settled in for the twenty-five-minute ride.

After the group's arrival at the processing center, the men were given assigned bunks at nearby quarters and told to wait for orders. The noncommissioned officer in charge briefed them. "Be sure you check the bulletin board in your barracks for departure dates and times. You may leave tomorrow morning or you may be here for at least three days. Don't miss your flight. No flights will be posted or will depart after 1800 hours. If you are not in a roster for a flight, after that you can get a pass to visit town or any nearby area. You must sign out at the orderly room or operations center. Are there any questions?"

Nobody responded.

"You can go and pick up your bedding equipment for tonight at Building 1053. The supply sergeant will give it to you, and you must turn it in if your name is posted for departure. Dismiss."

Hicks called Torres and said, "My amigo, tonight we can go check the city out. I have some friends I want to see before I go. I was stationed at Fort Ord, and I used to come around here. Also, you may meet some Spanish-Mexican senoritas and have a good time. They are really nice and friendly, and you may not see another for a long time. I know some Spanish. We'll drink cerveza and tequila. I like the drink that has the worm inside. I bite the worm; I wish it is alive."

Torres said, "Okay. We'll go, but you'd better behave or we'll end up in jail. Don't look for trouble unless you want me to quit on you."

"Don't worry. I know what to do, amigo," Hicks replied.

Around 1700 hours, both men dressed up, after taking a bath. Hicks and Torres ate at the NCO mess, then walked back and went directly to the orderly room to sign out for their intended visit to town. The charge of quarters said, "You must be here by 0530 hours and sign in."

It was already 1900 hours, and both men thought it was an appropriate time to leave if they wanted to be in early, no later than 2300 hours.

They walked to the front gate and Hicks asked one of the military policeman, "Where can we get a cab to go downtown?"

"Just stand here. They stop frequently," he answered.

"Thanks," Hicks said.

They walked up about twenty yards from the gate. Almost immediately a cab stopped and both men got in. Hicks told the driver, "Take us to a nice Spanish cantina where we can have cold cerveza and listen to some good, sweet Spanish music. Listen, Torres, I know how to sing Spanish. Listen, my friend. Alla en el rancho grande. Alla donde bebia."

Torres said, "Hey, Hicks, you don't say *bebia*. That means 'to drink.' You must say *vivia*, which means 'living.'"

"Well, it's all the same—drinking and living," Hicks replied.

"You and your crazy Spanish," Torres said.

"I know some German, too. Did you know I know how to speak German, Torres? I bet you didn't know I knew other languages, did you?"

Torres asked, "What German do you know? Tell me."

Hicks replied, "When I go to a bar, I say 'Lowenbrau.'"

Torres laughed.

The cab stopped at the side of a narrow street and the driver said, "Here you are. This is a good place, and it's very safe. Not many people, but you'll like it."

Hicks gave the driver $5 and told him to keep the change. They both got out of the cab.

The sign in front of the bar read, CANTINA. VINOS, CIGARI-LLOS, AND GOOD MUSIC.

Both men walked in. They noticed that the saloon was quite large but not wide. There were five people inside. Three young men were sitting at the far end to the right. Next to them was a sign pointing toward a corridor, indicating where the men's room was. The ladies' room was on the opposite side. An old man was sitting in the center of the saloon, sorting and checking some papers that were spread over the table in front of him. There was a portfolio to his right and various drawings and colored pencils lined up to his left. His table was almost in line with a huge mirror that was behind the bar, where a young lady bartender was standing washing some glasses and checking the liquor dispensers attached to the bottles.

The three young men had beers resting on the table and were drinking out of the bottles. There was a bottle of wine and a glass sitting on the old man's table, from which he seemed to be drinking. The music box was playing a Mexican ballad familiar to Torres. It was called "El Revolutionario," meaning "The Revolutionary" and the singer was one of Torres's favorites—Cuco Sanchez.

When Torres and Hicks walked in, everyone glanced at them. The two men walked to the bar and sat in the center in line with the huge mirror. "Buenos dias, Senorita. We need two cervezas," Hicks said.

The place was very clean and everything seemed to be in order. The three young men were talking loudly. By their accents and looks, they were of Mexican-Spanish descent. The old man was also Spanish. The young lady behind the bar was Mexican and probably in her late twenties.

After Hicks had ordered the beers, she said, "Good evening, I am Rosita but most people call me Rosie. I have Mexican beer, Corona. I also have American beer. I will give you two Coronas. They are good; you will like them. Do you want glasses?"

Hicks said, "No, I'll drink mine from the bottle." Torres asked for a glass.

Rosie served the beers and asked, "How about some tomato juice. Here we call it a Bloody Mary when you mix beer with it. It's not the same as the Bloody Mary the Americans drink; this one won't get you drunk. Are you stationed around here?"

"No," Hicks said. "We're on our way to Vietnam. We just stopped by."

Torres said, "Give me some tomato juice. I'll try it with my beer. How about you, Hicks?"

"Not me," he said. "I won't mix my beer. When I want something red in my beer, I'll cut my wrist and squeeze some blood out. I only drink tomato juice for breakfast and only in the army. Back home I drink moonshine and beer for breakfast. It tastes better."

Meanwhile, Mexican corridos and ballads were playing on the music box, and one of the three young men walked over and made some selections.

Rosie asked, "Where are you from Sarge?" looking at Torres.

"I'm from Puerto Rico; my friend here is from the state of Texas. We may leave tomorrow, and we wanted to see the city and have a cold beer. Where are you from?"

"I am from Tijuana. I am a naturalized citizen and my husband is a *gavacho*."

Hicks, listening to the conversation, said, "Your husband is a garbanzo? Why did you marry a bean? Who wants to marry a bean? Why would a woman do that?"

"My husband is not a bean; he is not a garbanzo. He is a *gavacho*, like you. We call the American-born men *gavachos*. You are a *gavacho*, and it is not a bad word," she said, smiling.

Hicks said, "So I am one of those too? If you say so. I've been called worse. I won't get mad. Well, anyway, you love your husband, he loves you, and that's all that counts."

50

"Yes, I do," Rosie replied. "He will come here later and pick me up when we close, just before midnight."

Hicks finished his beer and immediately stood up from his chair. "I have to go, Torres. If you want to stay, it's okay with me. If you want to come with me, that too is fine. I may stop here on my way back. I want to see my friends. I'll get a cab. They must be waiting for me. I called them and told them I would probably stop by. If I don't show up here in a couple of hours, don't wait for me. Take care of yourself. Maybe Rosie's *gavacho* will not show up and you can take her with you. She may say *adios* to him," he added jokingly.

"Good-bye, Sarge," Rosita said.

"Hey, Hicks," Torres said, "don't try to get me in trouble; the lady is married. You'd better get out of here before we both get run out. Go and see your friends and take care. Don't get drunk; we may leave tomorrow. It's a long trip and we need the rest, my friend. I'll be here if you come back soon. Adios, amigo."

Hicks walked to the front door and once more said, "Good-bye, everyone."

The old man had apparently been listening to some of the conversation and now said, "Vaya con Dios."

Torres had noticed the old man glancing in their direction once in a while. In a meticulous way, he had been tracing lines over a white sheet of paper. At times he momentarily stopped and scrubbed over the same paper as though making corrections in his writing or drawing. His hair was slightly white at the temples. A dry and thin complexion with a quixotic appearance indicated his ancestral and cultural pride. His glances at the huge mirror were consistent, and he was apparently very absorbed in his work.

The music stopped and Torres excused himself to the lady bartender and walked over to select some of the tunes he had heard while at the bar. He reached into his pocket and pulled out a quarter. Depositing it in the box, he made some selections

51

from the popular variety he found, "Cielito Lindo," "Adelita," and "Lonesome Cowboy" among them.

Torres glanced in the direction where the three young men were seated and walked toward the bathroom corridor. As he passed by the men, he greeted them, "Buenos dias, muchachos." They did not answer nor did they bother to look up.

Torres continued walking down the corridor. When he came out of the bathroom, the three men were walking in his direction, side by side. The young man in the center, who was about twenty years old, said, "Okay, amigo, this is not a holdup. Stay calm; nothing will happen to you. We won't hurt you."

Torres was surprised by the men's attitude and noticed that the same man who was doing the talking held a knife in his hand. Their attitudes were menacing, and Torres thought that he would not take any chances. They had said that it was not a holdup and not to worry. *What do they want?* he thought.

Suddenly the young man in the center said, "Leave Rosie alone. We don't want to hurt you. Don't think about making out with her; she's my girlfriend, okay? I like her and she is mine."

Torres said, "Are you her husband? I haven't tried to get a date with her or even said anything rude. My friend and I came here to have a couple of drinks and I'll be leaving very shortly. Don't worry about me taking Rosie away from you; I'm a married man and Hispanic like you. We talk the same language."

The young leader said once more, "Okay, but you must go right now. I don't want anyone talking to her."

Meanwhile, none of the men had noticed a figure approaching them from their rear. In a very discreet way the shadow closed in. Holding a curved knife about six inches long in his right hand, the figure came closer.

The men suddenly realized they were not alone and recognized the man with the knife in his hands. They immediately changed their attitudes. The old man, who moments before had been tracing lines, was standing in a very determined way, challenging the group in front of Torres. He said, "You bandoleros better get out of here and never bother to come back. If you hurt the soldier, I will kill all of you. I am an old man. I don't care if I die right now, but I'll take a couple of you with me. You don't have too much time to think about it. I knew you were up to something, you hoodlums. I am old and have served my time. You'd better go right now."

The group leader recognized that the old man meant business and said, "We have not hurt the soldier. He is a good friend. We were just playing around. He is our friend." His mood was preoccupied and the other two, meanwhile, had pressed themselves against the side of the wall to the right, as if they were going to run away.

"I heard everything you were saying to him. The soldier has not bothered anyone. He is not messing with the girl, and if she likes him it is her business. Rosie is a decent girl and I know her husband. You are trying to intimidate the sergeant for a woman you do not have any right to. Now get out of here before I get madder. If you come back, I will make you pay for it. I can kill you like dogs."

Rosie noticed that something was happening in the hallway and looked over from her location behind the bar. Being cautious she did not walk over in case she had to call the police.

As soon as the old man finished his last remarks, the three young men walked by him, keeping their distance. Without hesitating, they walked out of the saloon; they did not even glance back.

Torres, thankful for the old man's actions, said to him, "Gracias, Senor. I really do appreciate your help. You risked your life for me. I don't even know you, and you don't even know me."

The old man answered, "Oh, that was nothing! They are just young bandoleros who don't understand respect. They have to be challenged."

"I don't know why they accosted me. I don't like trouble,

and I haven't offended anyone. I was just talking to the lady; she is a very kind person," Torres said.

The old man walked out of the corridor, followed by Torres. As they cleared it, he said, shaking his head, "I know it. But you see, some men in this world fall in love at a glance. A lo adivino, as we say in Spanish. The young man with the knife is like that.

"What a life! People killing themselves in Vietnam. That is where you said you were going? I wish you health and good luck. There is no peace anywhere anymore, and it is probably safer where you are going that in some streets here in America. I remember my family in Mexico. There was some peace, not much, but there was some. I remember my great uncle. I was a boy then. People used to respect him. He died in 1923. People still remember him; he was a great fighter."

The old man walked back to his table and Torres returned to his seat. Rosie asked, "Is everything okay? I was worried. Is anything wrong? Those three young men left in a hurry. What happened back there?"

The old man answered from his location, "Oh, nothing, Rosita. Nothing, my young lady. Some youngsters do not like to respect other people and don't know how to behave. Everything is taken care of. Do not worry."

Rosita said to Torres, "Normally there are more people in here, but there is a religious fair in the park about ten blocks from here. Maybe some people will come later, although it is pretty late already. On weekends we use two bartenders in here to take care of the customers."

Torres, very pleased by the old man's actions, asked Rosita, "Rosie, what would he like to drink? Bring him a bottle, and you have a drink on me, too. I might sit with him; I will ask him. Give me a bottle of wine."

"That is what he likes to drink, but he likes to sit by himself. He loves muscatel and he likes to draw. I'll be back. Let me bring him the bottle myself. I'll tell him that you are sending it to him, and I'll also ask him if he wants you to join him."

She walked out from behind the bar and placed the bottle on the table in front of the old man. She leaned over and said something to him.

The old man said, "Thank you, Sergeant. Stay where you are and talk to Rosita. I am leaving very shortly. You will not see girls for a long time after you leave here; you are going to war. Enjoy yourself and talk to Rosita. You are young and can talk about many things."

Rosita walked back and stood behind the bar while the old man lifted his glass in sign of a toast, saying, "Salud!" He then took a quick sip of his wine. Torres did the same at his seat.

Rosita once more asked Torres, "What happened back there?"

"The three young men who were seated over there tried to scare me. One of them thought that I was trying to court you, and he said that you belong to him. He pulled a short knife. Then Grandpa walked over and, after a short talk, they ran like rabbits. I don't think they'll be back here for a while, at least not tonight. The old man scared the hell of them, as you saw."

"Very silly fellows. If they come here again, I'll throw them out. Thank you for the drink you offered me. I'll take it now. I drink tequila with orange juice. It is not a drink for everyone, but I like it."

Rosita poured herself a drink and asked Torres, "Have you ever been in Oakland before?"

"Yes, I was. Many years ago, when I was coming back from the Korean War. I even remember the ship I sailed in; she was called the SS *Fred C. Ainsworth*. She docked at the terminal and sailed up San Francisco Bay. There was a band waiting at the pier and they started to play before we'd even docked. I also remember a lady actress called Gloria Swanson. She sang a song called 'My Hero.'

"You know, I wonder. . . before the soldiers were sent to war with music, hugs and kisses. In San Juan, when I left for Korea during the war, the mayor of San Juan, a lady named Felisa Rincon, came over and hugged some of us. There was a musical group directed by a well-known musician named Jimenez. They played a guaracha called 'La Pulguita,' 'the Little Flea.' When we arrived in Korea, they received us there with music also, playing a song called 'White Lilies.' It tells the story about a girl left behind. She becomes a prostitute, working for a pimp, a very meaningful story."

Rosie smiled and said, "Well those things happen sometimes in real life. Anything is possible when people don't care."

"That depends on the kind of woman a man marries," Torres affirmed. "I was also lucky when I came here before because I won a $500 jackpot in a bingo game at the base. I bought my first car with the money."

Torres looked over at the old man, who was eagerly drawing. He said to Rosie, "Grandpa must be doing a masterpiece; he is drawing something."

The old man stood up and walked over to the bar where Torres was sitting. He handed him a paper with his portrait. He said to Torres, "It is not a masterpiece, but it is for you. You may send it back home to your wife; she may like to frame it. I did the best I could. I am getting old and can't see as well as I used to."

Torres took the drawing and was astonished at the old man's work. He had drawn him, insignias, uniform, face, and all. He said, "You were drawing me! It looks great, sir. Thank you a lot. I'll send it to my family. A thousand thanks."

Rosie said, "I did not want to tell you, but he only draws people he likes. I knew he was painting you all along. It looks great with those patches and everything on your shirt."

"I must go now, my friend," the old man said. He walked back to his table and started to collect his materials. After placing them inside his portfolio, he took another sip of his wine.

Rosie said to Torres, "I'm going to tell you something else. Everyone knows him around here. He is a descendant of a very famous person. He is the nephew of Francisco Villa, better known as Pancho Villa. He is the son of Villa's youngest sister."

"Whoaaa!" Torres said. "No wonder he said something about an uncle when we were walking back from the corridor."

The old man walked toward the front door, and Torres quickly asked Rosie, "Please, quickly, will you give me a bottle of muscatel? I want Senor Villa to take it with him."

Rosie immediately picked up a bottle and handed it to Torres. He grabbed it and walked toward Villa, who was almost at the exit. He handed it to him and said, "I know you deserve this and more. Thanks for your kind favors. I won't forget you. I will tell my children and all my family and friends about you. Vaya con Dios. Adios, le dice Villa."

"Gracias," the old man answered and walked down the empty street, vanishing into the night. Torres walked back toward the bar and said to Rosie. "What a man! He surely is a wonderful person."

"He calls me 'Nena,' which means little girl. I don't know if he has a wife or family. He comes here very often, and as I said, everyone likes him."

Torres stood up and said, "I don't think my friend Hicks is coming back. It's late and I'd better be going. Will you call me a cab? Also, will you be okay by yourself?"

"Sure, why not? I have been by myself before, and the bar owner and my husband should be here any minute. I know how to take care of myself. Don't worry." She walked to the phone and called for a cab. "It will be here any minute," she said.

Soon, the noise of an engine was heard outside, indicating the cab had arrived. Torres got up from his seat and pulled money from his wallet to pay Rosie for the drinks. He said, "Don't worry, Nena. Keep the change and have a drink with your gavacho. It's been a pleasure to know you and the old man. You are a beautiful and nice woman. I hope I can come this way again in the future."

Rosie walked around from behind the long bar. She stood in front of Torres, who was adjusting his soldier's hat. She looked straight at him. "The pleasure has been mine. I wish you and I could be single; I would not let you go. I would marry you and go to Puerto Rico. I want to wish you the best. Take care of yourself. You said that you are going to be an advisor in Vietnam; you will come back, I know."

The lady moved close and placed her arms around Torres's shoulders. Pulling herself up, she kissed him on both cheeks. "God be with you. You will come back from the war. I want to see you again and have a drink with you once more. Vaya con Dios." Her eyes brightened and grew wet as if she wanted to cry but did not want to show her emotions.

Torres said, "Thank you, Rosie. Thanks for your blessings. I'll be back. If I can advise others to have a drink in here and meet nice people, I'll do it. I'll advise the bad guys to stay away from Villa; I don't think they'd have a chance."

Rosie smiled, "You'd better go. The cab is waiting. Good-bye."

"Good-bye," Torres said and walked out just as the cab driver was coming to the door to check for his customer.

The taxi took Torres back to the base after a twenty-five-minute ride. He walked out and handed the driver a five-dollar bill. "Keep the change, amigo." Then Torres walked toward the gate, showed his ID, and proceeded to his sleeping quarters. In his mind he thought only of Villa, Rosie, and the folded picture he carried in his left hand. He wanted to send it to Elsa back home and tell her to frame it. Many, many thoughts were in his mind.

6

The charge of quarters was walking, pushing the light switches on. He loudly announced, "Time to get up. Everybody up. Let's go. Everyone waiting for orders to travel to Vietnam check the bulletin board for postings and announcements. Check your flight number and time of departure. Go to breakfast if you want. If you have any questions, go to the orderly room or the operations center. Okay, everyone up."

Torres sat up and glanced toward Hicks's bed to check if he had arrived. He saw a bundle wrapped up like a pile of dirty laundry waiting to be picked up. He knew Hicks was in and, as usual, wrapped up from head to toe. He also heard him snoring. He shouted loudly, "Come on, gavacho. It's time to get up. We're leaving today. Let's go, Hicks, get up."

Rolling over, Hicks said, "Don't bother me, Torres. Let the war last for a little longer. I already said I'm going to end it when I get there. Let the gooks live a little longer." He moaned and groaned as he sat up.

"Yeah, you may end up in the stockade if you don't get ready. We can't miss the flight," Torres said. He added, "You had a good time last night with your friends and so did I. I waited for you, but it got late and I took a cab back here."

"You mean you didn't stay with Rosita and make her forget her garvanzo for the night?"

"Come on, Hicks. You know she's a good girl. I'll tell you later what happened. You won't believe it. I'm glad you went to look for your friends because you may have ended up fighting with the three fellows that were sitting by the corner."

59

"What? Did they give you trouble?"

"No. The old man took care of it. If we don't fly out of here tonight, I'll go back there tonight. I want you to meet the old man. He may paint you. I'll show you the picture he did of me. Very beautiful and realistic."

"Oh, yeah. I want statues of me, not pictures. A hero. Right in the middle of Texas," Hicks said.

Torres laughed, while Hicks stood up and stretched his arms upward and said, "I need a shower and then a beer."

"A what? You are an alcoholic. A beer for breakfast. Only alcoholics do that, Hicks."

Hicks replied, "I had a hell of a time with my friends. They didn't want me to leave. They brought me in about 0400 hours. Girls, dancing, good music, and booze. What a life!"

"If I stay here one more day, I'll go crazy, Torres."

Both men picked up towels and shaving kits and walked toward the shower room. Hicks continued with his jokes, past adventures, and his fantasies about ending the war in Nam, while Torres listened. Hicks was a very high-spirited character. Anyone listening to him got an earful and wondered about Hicks's mental status.

The two walked to the mess where they had breakfast. As usual, Hicks drank a couple of cups of coffee; he said he needed to stay awake. Soon after, they walked back to the orderly room. They checked the board while they walked to the mess hall, but no orders had been posted yet.

The next time Torres and Hicks checked the board they found their names on a list scheduled to leave at 0900 hours. It was not much time, but after all, they were already packed and ready. They would depart on a commercial plane, Continental Airlines. The plane would make stopovers in Alaska and Japan.

Buses arrived on time to pick the soldiers up and drop them at the San Francisco Airport. They would be flying from across the bay and they had to cross the Golden Gate Bridge. It was a long ride, and for some of the men it was good; they could snap pictures with cameras as they rode by.

They arrived at the airport without any delays. There they received instructions to pick up their baggage and report to a waiting area where only military personnel were allowed. They had to pick up their boarding tickets and process their baggage. From there they boarded the plane. They were going to fly in style to the war—with beautiful hostesses and warm meals until they reached their destination, Ton Shong Nhut Airbase.

All the passengers aboard were military except for the plane crew. Instructions for emergencies, as usual, were given and information about stops to refuel. "We wish all of you a pleasant trip," were the last words heard from the plane's loud-speakers, in the sweet and pleasant voice of a hostess.

The flight was without delay, other than the already planned stopovers to pick up food and gas. There were also changes of crews. The International Dateline was crossed once more, and the men changed the dates on their calendars.

It was September 27, at 1100 hours, when the plane landed at Ton Shong Nhut Airbase. Already there were military buses waiting for the men. It was a very clear day. The men peeped out of the plane windows with curiosity for their first look at Vietnam. They saw nothing abnormal or out of place as the plane taxied to a sudden stop and they started to unbuckle their seat belts and reach for their hand bags and camera cases, which had been placed in the compartments above their seats.

The plane's right door was opened and already steps had been put in place that the passengers would be walking down. As they did, they were told by a sergeant waiting at the bottom, dressed in camouflage fatigues, to walk to a nearby building and, as they entered, to take a seat.

The men proceeded to follow the orders after securing their

personal baggage, which was being unloaded and moved in a cart to the front of the building. There were buses lined up to the right of the building, and some military jeeps managed by military police and security forces were also standing nearby.

Torres could not miss the security around the area. There were concertina wires and observation towers, with guards managing positions where machine guns were mounted on tripods all around. Sandbags had been placed around the buildings. There were also some bunkers. Planes were taking off and landing at intervals of three to five minutes. It seemed to be a very busy airport.

A sign demanded the attention of the men as they entered the appointed building. It had arrows with writing on them. Each of the arrows pointed in a different direction: an arrow pointing to Tokyo, one to Paris, one to San Francisco, and last but not least, one to Hanoi. Who wanted to go to Hanoi? Maybe it was a reminder to be aware and not become a prisoner of war.

After the men had entered and sat down, instructions and names were called. All men assigned to MACV (military assistance command Vietnam) were separated and lined up to be loaded onto buses. No one knew where they were going except for the operations members and the drivers of the buses. The buses had screens for security outside the window glasses. An escort jeep accompanied the bus in front as it exited the area. The military bus driver had weapons strapped to the left side of the driver's seat.

The buses passed by a park, where a huge statue of two women was standing. Torres recognized it and explained its meaning to Hicks, who was seated by his side. "Those two women are a symbol to the people here. They are the Truong sisters, who were killed by Chinese, according to the stories. They are heroines."

Hicks, in his permanent joking tone, said, "You know, Torres, I came here to end this war, and they may erect a statue of me out here. But check out those people pulling the carts." He was watching the rickshaws going by. "Those guys all look alike, and I can't figure myself riding in one of them."

"Why, Hicks?" Torres snapped back.

"Well, whatever they are called, and personally I don't care, I'm a heavy guy and I don't want a Vietnamese pulling me from the front. He'll be puffing and snuffling for air, but above all, he'll be backfiring from his ass at me. I don't want to smell anyone's shit. I'm too heavy. I'd like to go to the president of Vietnam and tell him that the war will be over soon—I'm here."

Torres laughed; then he said, "You'd better keep your eyes open when you get to the field. I hope they'll assign us to the same team."

The buses kept rolling along the narrow streets of the Saigon district until they came to a stop in front of a building with a sign that read KOELPNER COMPOUND, MACV COMMAND. At the front there were Vietnamese policeman, accompanied by military American and Vietnamese policemen. One of the guards signaled the buses to proceed through the gate. The bus drivers drove their vehicles into the compound. Inside the compound was like a patio surrounded by decorator palms with benches in-between.

The men were told to exit the vehicles after each came to a full stop. The area had the appearance of a Spanish villa. The building, with its squared patio, was three floors in height, with open corridors in front of all of them.

While the men secured their equipment, the bus drivers drove the vehicles away. A U.S. Army sergeant first class came to meet the men and said, "After you get your equipment, follow me to the briefing room." The room was located in the west wing.

Each man carried his own bags and placed them along the corridor of the lower floor near the briefing room. The men walked inside the room as the sergeant had ordered and imme-

63

diately proceeded to sit in the chairs lined up in rows. They waited for further orders as another sergeant was standing behind a podium directing the men to fill all the seats to the front. The podium was placed in front of the chairs.

After each had taken a seat, a captain walked behind the podium and said, "Welcome to Saigon and Koelpner Compound. I am Captain Morris, assistant operations officer in this compound. The instructions you will receive here must be complied with. You may be staying here for two or more days or until your processing is completed. Afterward you will be shipped out to your next station or unit of assignment.

"Some of you may go to the 4th, 3rd, 2nd, or 1st Corps. They are located throughout the country. Any personal matters will be taken care of by the administrative and operations personnel here; we have all the necessary facilities to handle them.

"Your rooms are ready. You will be issued equipment at the supply facilities. The sergeant will give you your room numbers. There will be two men to a room. Any questions?

"If there are no questions, thank you for your attention and good luck."

After the captain concluded, the sergeant proceeded to call the room numbers for each man. "Hey, Hicks, I hope we'll be together. Maybe we could get assigned to the same team. We'll know by tomorrow where we'll be going. By the way, I saw Melendez here."

"Who is Melendez?" Hicks asked Torres.

"Oh, he's the Spanish guy who was with us at Fort Bragg. Once you see him, you'll remember. He probably got here ahead of us. He wasn't on our flight. Others may get here soon.

"I'm having problems with this upper front tooth," Torres added. "I'd better take care of it before I leave here. I must find out where the dental clinic is after I put my stuff in the room."

Both men walked up the stairs to the second floor in the west wing of the compound. Their rooms were located almost above the briefing room. After Torres found his assigned room, which was next to Hicks's, he put his bags inside and walked out into the corridor. He saw Melendez coming in his direction. Torres asked, "When did you get here? I just told Hicks about you. He doesn't remember you. How are you?"

"I'm fine, Torres. I got here about two hours ahead of your group. My bed is the one across from yours; we're in the same room."

Hicks walked out of his room and, approaching both men, said, "Now I remember you; we were in the same section. Torres told me about seeing you downstairs."

Torres asked Melendez, "Did you get your assignment yet?"

"I did. I'm assigned to the 4th Corps, but I'm going to see if I can change it to the 1st. I have a cousin up there; they may do it," Melendez said.

The 4th Corps was located in the Delta, which was the area southwest of Saigon.

The three men walked downstairs together and decided to check out the facilities around the compound. They stopped in front of the post exchange, the cafeteria, and other shops located on the first floor of the building. Torres said to Hicks and Melendez, "I must go to the dental clinic now. I'll see you fellows later. We could get together for supper, if I can still chew anything. I don't think it will take too much time. At least, I hope not."

Torres walked away toward the main office to ask for the clinic's location. He was told that the clinic was located off the compound and that he was to walk through the gate and around the corner to find it. It was open. It was located in the center of the left wing on the first floor facing the street. Torres walked in and the nurse asked, "Can we help you, Sarge?"

"Yes, Lieutenant. I have a loose filling in my top front tooth and I hope the dentist can fix it for me."

"We'll see. Let's get some X rays first. Afterwards we have

to fill these papers in for your records. You turned in your medical and dental records at the operations room and this will be added to them later."

The nurse took X rays, and after a short wait, Torres was called in and told to sit in the dentist's chair. A captain said to him, "You're going to join an advisory team, I imagine. I'll fix your tooth and hope that it lasts. I have to put a pin in it. It won't take long. Don't chew hard stuff for a couple of days, then afterwards you may eat some *khong cho*."

The dentist started to drill. After hammering a metal pin, he attached the mold to secure the filling. He waited a few minutes until it had hardened, then sanded it.

"Everything is done. Now you can go out there and later eat your *khong cho*, as I said. For now take it easy. Don't bite anything hard for at least three days. The filling will last at least until you get out of here. It's just temporary, but it will do if you're careful."

"Thanks a lot, Doctor. I'll be careful. I know some Vietnamese, but I don't know what *khong cho* is. What is it, Doctor?"

"No, I won't tell you. You'll find out soon enough."

Torres returned to his room where he found Melendez. "How was your trip to Puerto Rico?" Torres asked.

"Fine. I visited all my relatives and had a good time. I hope this year here goes quickly. We'd better look around for your friend Hicks. He told me he would be at the cafeteria and to meet him there. He's kind of wild sometimes. I know you and he get along very well, but sometimes he worries people. I hope he takes care of himself," Melendez said.

The two men walked out of the room and headed for the cafeteria, where Hicks was drinking a cup of coffee and waiting for them to return. They walked through the serving line and picked out their food, sitting down at the same table with Hicks.

"We'd better go and check if our assignment orders are

ready. They should be. It's already six o'clock and the word is that we must check for them," Torres said.

They got up and headed for the operations room. There other members of the military were checking for their orders as well, and they had to stand in line. The line was moving very fast as the men picked up their orders and stepped quickly out of the room.

"Look, I got assigned to the 1st Corps. What's yours?" Torres asked Hicks.

"I'll be with Melendez in the 4th Corps. We may end up working on the same team. But as I said, I'll finish this war. Don't worry, guys, I'm here now, and everything will be over soon."

Melendez said, "I said I wanted to go to the 1st Corps. I may still have the chance. How about you and me trading assignments, Torres?"

The military advisory command in Vietnam (MACV) had their assigned teams of advisors operating throughout Vietnam. The teams were identified by numbers, and in the 1st Corps operating to the north were Team One, Team Two, Team Three, etc.

After receiving his orders, Torres went to pick up some military equipment that he had to carry with him upon leaving the compound. He was issued fatigue jackets of the so-called safari style and other necessary clothes. He was given patches to be sewn on the left sleeve of his jackets, with others to be hung from the bottom of the left pocket of his shirts and jackets. A folder was issued to him describing the meaning of the figures and colors of the patches.

The MACV insignia consisted of a sword with a yellow hilt and a white blade. The blade was pointing up between two segments of a yellow arched emblematic fess, or horizontal bar, across a field drawn over a red shield three inches high, all within a one-eighth-inch yellow border.

67

The meaning of the insignia was written inside the folder. The yellow and red represented the Vietnamese flag colors. The red also represented infiltration and oppression and was blocked by the sword, representing U.S. military aid and support. The wall was arched and the sword pointing upward in reference to the offensive action pushing the attackers back. It could not be worn outside the country when worn as a patch on the pocket, but it could be worn on the sleeve of military uniforms.

All the military personnel were issued jungle fatigues, including a safari hat. Among the other equipment issued were a gas mask, ammunition belt, helmet with liner, first-aid kit, two canteens with covers, two pairs of jungle boots, and an M14 7.62-millimeter rifle.

7

Early the next day all the men going north got their traveling tickets and Torres said good-bye to his friends. Among the group going with Torres were two more companions of his from the Special Warfare School, Marine Sergeant Arce and U.S. Army Sergeant First Class Oshiro. Both had been assigned to serve with the 1st Corps. All of them were taken to Camh Rah Bay Airbase. They would be flown north from there aboard a 130 cargo plane. Hicks and Melendez were due to depart for the Delta the next day.

After the men were bused to Camh Rah Bay Airbase, located to the north of Saigon, they were boarded onto the plane. The flight up north took off on schedule, and from the air the men closer to the windows could see the high mountains and the greenish texture of the jungles below. Outposts could easily be distinguished by their cream and bald appearance on top of hills. The plane was flying very high as a precaution to avoid hostile fire from below.

On the way it landed at the city of Qui Nhon, which is located about halfway between Saigon and Da Nang. Some men got off the plane. Qui Nhon was under the control of the 2nd Corps.

The plane continued its flight north, and everyone aboard secured their seat straps as a precautionary measure in case the plane was fired upon. The plane had other cargo to the rear, secured with straps and tie rings attached to the floor.

The craft landed at Da Nang Airbase, which was located a short distance to the south of the city. The base was well-secured, guarded by American marines. Da Nang used to be called Tourane and being close to North Vietnam was susceptible to attack by the North Vietnamese Army as well as the Vietcong.

Buses were waiting at the airbase, and the plane passengers walked out and down the rear ramp of the cargo bay after each had secured their personal baggage. The men boarded the buses as directed by the drivers, who were U.S. Army, and took off for the city.

The vehicles came to a stop in front of a hotel that looked similar to the one at the MACV Compound in Saigon. It was only a little smaller and two stories high. The patio was not as big inside. U.S. Marines were in charge of security, and no civilian or military Vietnamese policemen were in sight.

The men disembarked from the buses and were assigned rooms. They were told to wait for instructions. After one day at the compound, they were taken to the 1st Corps Operations Center to receive orders of assignment. Torres was assigned to serve with the 2nd Advisory Team located in Quang Ngai, south of Da Nang. Quang Ngai was also the capital of the province that carried the same name. Besides Quang Ngai, the team also operated within the northern provinces of Quang Nam, Quang Tri, and Quang Tin.

Torres received all the necessary documentation, which included a military driver's license, a code of conduct card, and other assorted cards with information on military tactics and field-operations conduct, including rules of behavior for advisors, guidance for commanders in Vietnam, key Vietnamese phrases, the Geneva Convention rules, tips on Vietcong and North Vietnamese mines and booby traps, and warnings about contraband.

After completing his processing at the 1st Corps Operations Center, Torres received instructions about leaving to join his unit. He was to be assigned to a still smaller team. Their mission was to advise and give the necessary logistics support to paramilitary and military forces. Torres's next assignment would be at the discretion of the Team Two commander once he got to Quang Ngai.

The next day Torres was picked up at the compound and taken to the same airbase he'd arrived at the day before. A U.S. Army plane used as a courier for mail and military passengers assigned to work in the city of Quang Ngai was waiting and ready to depart. It could accommodate fourteen passengers. The team was made up of a pilot, who was a captain; a copilot, who was a first lieutenant; and a specialist five, who acted as crew chief. All were U.S. Army. Torres was the only passenger aboard the plane.

The plane took off and flew toward the Yellow Sea. It followed the contour lines drawn by the shoreline in a southerly direction. It was not a high-altitude flying aircraft, and to prevent it from being exposed to any hostile groundfire by enemy forces, this was the most adequate route to follow.

About thirty minutes later, the plane started to descend and circled around toward land. It glided down smoothly and landed at a small airstrip. No difficulties were encountered in the operation, and the plane came to a stop in front of some bleachers, which apparently were used as a staging area for troop deployments.

There was a military jeep parked nearby. An Army specialist four walked toward the plane. Torres, who had already walked down the short stairs of the craft, was expecting someone to meet him. The specialist asked him, "Are you Sergeant Torres?"

"Yes, I am."

"Will you please come with me. I'll take you to the compound. Let me help you with your equipment."

"Thanks a lot," Torres said.

After they had loaded the gear into the rear seat of the quarter-ton truck, both men proceeded to climb aboard, Torres on the passenger's side.

"How far is the compound?" Torres asked.

"Not too far. About ten minutes. I'll show you some of the sights along the way. You may need to know about them in case you have to go to any of them in the future."

Torres glanced toward the left and right. He wanted to familiarize himself with the area. He saw straw houses, sugar cane fields, and rice paddies scattered along both sides of the road. High hills could be seen in the distance.

When the vehicle reached the city line, which was easily recognized by cement buildings and people walking around, the driver said to Torres, "This is the city of Quang Ngai. It is not a big city, more like a small American town. The main street is also part of Route 1, going north to south."

The cement buildings looked identical, with bunkers and trenches around many of them. There were guards dressed in military uniforms, all Vietnamese. There were machine guns mounted on tripods as well.

"There's the hospital," the driver said to Torres, pointing to the right, where a building with a Red Cross flag on a wooden pole was visible. There were two ambulances parked in front. A couple of buildings had American and Vietnamese flags standing side by side, which indicated that American agencies or military units were operating from those locations.

Kids were running around and women walked about in their customary Vietnamese-type dresses. Some wagons pulled by water buffalo were standing by the road and others were being pulled along by men. They were carrying rice straw tied in bundles. The buffalo were paired off and tied to yokes by their horns.

The young driver said to Torres, "You may see or maybe have already seen some Americans or Spanish-complexioned people. They work for USAID, the United States Agency for International Development. The Spanish could be doctors from Cuba. They're volunteers at the hospital. There are some religious organizations working around here also. They give assistance to the civilian population. You may see some of them around the compound."

As the jeep approached the main gate of the compound, Torres saw a long cement building well protected by barbed and concertina wire around the perimeter. There were also bunkers and sandbagged foxholes. Well-armed ARVN soldiers wore shoulder patches that identified them as military policemen. The patches read QUAN CANH.

The driver said to Torres, "That's Regimental Headquarters. The chief advisor of Team Two has his office there also. You'll probably be assigned to one of the battalions out in the field; they're spread all over the northern provinces."

The driver came to a stop in front of a gate. A sentinel's squared shack, with sandbags around it, was located to the left of the entrance and was guarded by two U.S. Marine security policemen and a Vietnamese civilian policeman. A guard, recognizing the driver, signaled to him to enter.

The specialist parked the jeep in front of a building with a distinctive sign that indicated the structure was the orderly room. It was a wooden building painted in yellow, with sandbags around the outside walls. There was also a sign with the first sergeant's name on it and another with the name of the captain who was the compound commander.

The driver pointed to the front door and said, "Just walk in through there. They're waiting for you. I'll take care of your bags until you come back."

"Thank you," Torres said.

Torres opened the front door and walked in. There a young specialist four was sitting behind a desk with a sign indicating he was the clerk. "Hello, I'm Sergeant Torres. Here are my assignment orders," Torres said, as he handed the clerk his orders.

The young man said, "Welcome to Quang Ngai and Team Two. We'll process you in as quickly as possible. The first sergeant will see you and talk to you."

The first sergeant walked out of a room that had a sign above the door indicating it was the compound commander's office. Walking toward Torres, he extended his right hand to shake Torres's while saying, "Welcome, Sergeant Torres. You may be here for a day or two. You'll join your team at an outpost near the city of Tam-Ky. It's north of here. You are assigned to Team Two, which is presently working with the 4th Battalion of the 5th Regiment of the 2nd Division. Tam-Ky is in Quang Tin province. A resupply helicopter will bring you to the team. I was in the field before I became first sergeant in this compound. Before you depart you'll get everything you may need and don't have up to now. The supply sergeant will give it to you. Come with me. I'll take you to your room for the time you will be here."

Both men walked out of the building, and Torres picked up one of the bags while the young driver, who was waiting, picked up the other and proceeded to follow Torres and the first sergeant. The first sergeant continued to brief Torres, pointing out along the way where the mess hall was, the mail office, and a small building used as a club. He said, "If you have any mail waiting for you, you can pick it up at the mail room after I show you your room."

The first sergeant stopped in front of a door about midway along a row of apartments that had the appearance of a stateside motel.

"This is your room. You don't need to lock it. The maids are very trustworthy people, and they are searched at the gate when they go home anyway. If you have any laundry that needs to be washed and pressed, one of the maids will do it for a small fee. Check with me before you pay any of them for any services. We don't want to spoil them. Also, be careful what you give them. No cigarettes or rations, no military pay scripts. We pay them in Vietnamese money.

"You can go to the club and drink a beer after 1800 hours. It is opened until 2100. I recommend you don't go out of the compound at night. It is not safe. Any questions?"

"No, First Sergeant. I understand."

"The next thing is to go to the supply room and pick up your bedding. Good luck and I'll see you later."

The first sergeant departed for his office, and Torres walked into the room and placed his bag on a bed located to the right. There was another bed to the left, which was also empty. The young man who had carried Torres's other bag had dropped it in front of the room.

Torres walked to the supply room. There he was issued a .45-caliber pistol, with a holster and ammunition. He was also given a compass, a grenade launcher, mosquito netting, a blanket, an air mattress, a sleeping bag with cover, a bayonet for his rifle, a flak jacket, and bedding to be used for the time he was going to stay. He knew he had to be ready to depart at any moment.

Torres walked to the mess hall, where he ate after paying for his meal. He was authorized to get a per-diem allowance and he had to pay for his own food. All members of the advisory groups were entitled to the extra pay. The armed forces provided such pay to any servicemen who did not have accessibility to military facilities where meals were provided free of charge. They were provided with funds equal to the value of the meals, and they had to buy their own food. Torres could buy cases of C rations, which are called combat rations and are properly canned. A case could support one person for eight days.

Torres decided to rest that evening and not visit the small club; he knew he had to be ready in the morning in case he had to depart and join his team.

He slept well and although he heard some weapons being fired in the distance, it did not bother him. Torres thought that in case of an attack to or near the compound, he would be properly alerted on time and moved to a defensive position around the compound. He got up early in the morning, took a shower, and then shaved as he had always done. Then he went to eat breakfast at the mess hall, where he met the first sergeant.

8

"Good morning, Sergeant Torres. I hope you slept well because you'll be departing at 1000 hours. You'll fly the resupply helicopter that brings the mail to the field. Get your stuff ready after you eat; the driver will bring you to the helipad. Any questions?"

"No. I'm ready," Torres said.

"You may come back here and get a job. It's normally done after you've been in the field awhile. Take care of yourself. Keep your head down and your eyes open. I may see you before I depart for home in about six months," the first sergeant added.

"Thank you, First Sergeant. I appreciate your advice, and I hope you get home safely," Torres said, after shaking hands.

Torres returned to his room immediately after eating. At 0900 hours the driver came to pick him up. After helping him load his equipment into the jeep, he drove Torres to the helipad.

The resupply chopper, a Huey with two machine guns mounted one on each side and managed by two U.S. Army gunners was ready to depart. The craft also had rocket launchers mounted on each side, each properly loaded with four rockets per launcher. It was piloted by a warrant officer and a copilot of the same rank.

After Torres had secured himself and all his equipment was aboard, the helicopter took off immediately with Torres as the only passenger.

From the air Torres could see isolated and half-destroyed villages. There were cement buildings among the structures with only one or two walls standing. Their roofs were destroyed. Rice paddies and sugar-cane fields were clearly visible, as the craft was not flying high. It was following the contour lines of Route 1, going in a northerly direction. Some military and civilian vehicles were running in both directions along the highway below. Damaged bridges and some rivers and streams could be seen. Some outposts, distinguished by their bold appearance, were noted. After flying for a half hour, the Marine base of Chulai came in sight, the many reinforced bunkers marking the perimeter. There were some artillery emplacements located at the base, as well as an outpost located to the left. Some combat ships were also docked at the maritime line of the Yellow Sea. Bulldozers and amphibious vehicles could be seen as the chopper continued its northerly flight toward Torres's team's location.

Suddenly the city of Tam-Ky came into sight. The helicopter circled to the left of the built-up area and aimed straight toward a hill, which apparently was the final destination for the moment for the single passenger. The craft had taken about forty-five minutes to get to Tam-Ky.

The helicopter landed at a marked helipad on top of a hill that seemed to be the most elevated one in the area. Torres had shouldered his M14 rifle and his H-frame pack before the chopper came to a complete halt. When the rotating blades came to a stop, he jumped out of the craft, dropping his weapon and pack at a safe distance. He returned to pick up his duffel bag and cargo pack, which one of the gunners handed to him.

"Thank you," he told the gunner and walked back to his pack and rifle.

A young Vietnamese walked toward Torres and very gracefully said, "Chao, Thuong Si Nhut, Da Co-Van. Thuong Si, Da Co-Van. I am Binshi Hoi. I like to help you, Da Co-Van."

"Thank you. Chao, Hoi. I am Sergeant Torres. I came here to be with you."

"You will be *Da Co-Van*, the Advisor. I am glad to know you. The others are at the bunker. I will help you carry the bag." Hoi smiled and picked up Torres's duffel bag. He seemed friendly.

The helicopter had begun to rotate its blades as a preliminary signal it was taking off. It slowly moved up vertically. Once it was about seventy-five feet up in the air, it gracefully swung into a northerly direction to deliver mail to some other advisory groups. Torres waved good-bye to the crew, and the gunners acknowledged by waving back at him.

Torres followed Hoi. From a bunker located almost center left, facing west, came a husky figure who, by his appearance, seemed to be of Native American ancestry. "Welcome to the team," he said. "I am Gunny Tim, a member of the Marine Corps and a member of the team also. We've known you were coming since yesterday. We got the message by radio. You've met Hoi already; he is our helper. He takes care of our equipment when we need him. The captain and the lieutenant are inside the bunker. With you there are now four of us. Follow me. I'll bring you to meet the rest of the team."

Torres shook hands with the marine and said, "Glad to meet you, Gunny Tim. Is that what I should call you?"

"Yes, everyone does. I'll call you Torres. Is that okay with you?"

"Sure, everyone calls me by my last name. I don't have a nickname. I'll do the most I can to help the team. I'm glad you came out to receive me; I thought for a while that no Americans were around."

"Oh no! We were getting some messages by radio. The captain has to go sometime, maybe today or tomorrow, to get orders and instructions on an operation that is in the planning stages. We'll find out soon," Gunny Tim said.

Torres followed the broad-shouldered marine into the bunker, which from the outside seemed to be large and well built. It had sandbagged walls, three to four bags in depth, and was capable of resisting the indirect hit of an M60 mm round from a mortar or rocket launcher. It was well fortified to resist an 81 mm mortar round from the top.

When Torres entered following Gunny Tim, a captain, who seemed to be in his early thirties, stood up from a chair and extended his hand to shake Torres's, saying, "Welcome to the 4th Battalion of the 5th Regiment and our team. I am Captain Johnson, the chief advisor. I'll brief you, and you can learn about the job from the rest of the team. You went to MATA and should know many things already. This is Lieutenant McDuffie; he's the second in command."

Torres shook hands and said, while saluting both men, "Glad to meet you, sirs. I hope to learn as much from you as I can. I was in the Korean War. Although I know things are different here, war is war, and I've seen death before. I'm a professional soldier, and I'll try to adjust as quickly as possible."

The captain said, "We are three army guys and a marine. We get along very well. We protect each other, and we never go alone on missions, or anywhere else for that matter. If something has to be done, we work in pairs, even if it's only going for supplies. Stay on the alert and keep your eyes open. You look out for me, and I'll look out for you.

"That will be your bed over there." He pointed to a cot that was located to Torres's left. "You'll pull radio watch at night; during the day we all monitor the radios. There are two of them, as you can see. Remember the code signs we use; you had better memorize them. Here's a notebook with some of them. Use the military alphabet when you have to spell anything out. Sometimes we use Jack Benny's age when sending coordinates for locations, although probably Charlie already knows what we're talking about." The captain was referring to the number thirty-nine, which Jack Benny always gave as his current age.

"I know what you mean, Captain," Torres said.

The bunker inside was big enough to accommodate six men or maybe more. The center was supported by an eight by eight pole holding up the roof. Around the pole was a built-in wooden table that the two radios rested on. There were also some military maps of the surrounding area on it.

The bunker had front and rear doors opposing each other, facing south and north respectively. There were two gas lamps and an electric wire with a light bulb attached to a socket at the end. The wire ran to the outside and was attached to a gasoline-powered generator.

The weapons and combat gear of each member of the team were suspended by nails driven into the wall beams supporting the structure. There were only two folding chairs, and some empty wooden ammunition boxes were nailed to the horizontal beams along the walls.

The ammunition boxes served as storage for extra rations, candles, hand grenades, flares, water-purification tablets, and other miscellaneous items. There was a small gas stove with a single burner and two five-gallon cans of water. Ammunition bandoleers were hanging from nails attached to the wall beams.

"Welcome once more to the team, Sergeant Torres," said the captain. "You met Tim already, and we're glad you're joining our team. We have been with the battalion for a while. You're replacing a member who was transferred to another team. You will learn everything. Take your time and do not worry. Is this your first trip here?"

"Yes, sir, but I have been in combat before. I was in Korea and have seen action before. I know this in here is different terrain, but I will be aware of any situation. I do catch on fast. I graduated from MATA school at Fort Bragg and also have ranger training. I know how the jungles look. I know some Vietnamese language from the school, and I will learn more from you."

The lieutenant, who was listening immediately said, "You'll get to know a lot, Sergeant. You'll see."

"Well, I'm not saying that I will become an expert overnight, but I know teamwork and how to be part of the team.

I will do the most to accomplish the missions. I will appreciate your help. Thanks to all of you."

"That is your bunk, Sergeant Torres." The captain pointed toward the bed to the left of the sergeant, who was still standing to the left of Gunny Tim, who was seated on the bunk directly opposite Torres's bed.

"I have to pick up my gear outside. Hoi is watching it," Torres said.

"If you need help, just holler," Gunny Tim said, as Torres walked out of the bunker.

"Thanks, Gunny. It's not much, and I think Hoi will help me."

Torres walked over to where he'd left his equipment with Hoi. "Da Co-Van, Thuong Si Nhut, Torres. Where are you from, Co-Van? You are not Bac Mi?" Hoi asked.

"Yes, I'm an American. I come from an island called Puerto Rico. It is a small island to the east of Cuba and east of Florida. I don't speak too much Vietnamese, but you are going to teach me and I can teach you Spanish. I speak Spanish."

"Okay, Co-Van. That is number one. Co-Van will be Hoi's teacher and Hoi will be Co-Van's teacher."

"I am a *binshi nhut*. It is private first class."

Torres took his H-frame pack and adjusted it to his back. He took his rifle and wrapped its sling over his right shoulder and with his left hand reached for his cargo pack. Hoi picked up the duffel bag, loaded it over his shoulder, and followed Torres into the bunker, where he placed it on Torres's bunk. Torres said, "Cam on, Hoi" ("Thank you, Hoi").

"You are welcome Co-Van," answered Hoi.

"Oh! You already know more Vietnamese than I knew when I arrived here. Hoi is very helpful and reliable. Other soldiers here are jealous of him because he travels with us and we take him to town sometimes. He likes to speak English, and he is learning. You'll meet some others who speak some English, too," Gunny Tim said to Torres.

"Sergeant Torres," the captain said, "are you ready to meet the battalion commander? He is a major and we call him Thiuta Thang. He was a Vietminh once. Let's go and see him. I will present you also to Bam Bah, which means the S-3, or operations, personnel. You will meet the others at a later date."

Torres said, "Okay, sir, I'm ready. I'll follow you."

Both men walked out of the bunker, Torres following the officer, who walked around the position in the direction of a huge bunker which, by its appearance, indicated it was the battalion commander's operations bunker. Long radio antennas could easily identify its location, along with various field telephone wires running from the location to other fortified positions.

Captain Johnson walked in with Torres immediately behind him. He said to a Vietnamese lieutenant, "Lieutenant, this is Sergeant Torres. He will be with the team. He just arrived. Where is Thiuta Thang?"

"Thiuta will be here in a minute. He went to his sleeping bunker. Chao, Sergeant Torres. I am happy to see you. I speak some English. I am the chief of operations. Anything that I can help you with I will do it, Co-Van."

"Thank you, sir. I'll try to help you, too. I am also glad to meet you."

A middle-aged and stocky officer walked in. He was about five feet in height, as were many of the Vietnamese soldiers.

"Oh, here is Thiuta," said the captain. "Thiuta, this is Sergeant Torres. He is with our team now."

Torres stood to attention and vigorously snapped a military salute to the officer, who acknowledged it by bringing his right arm and cupped fingers up to his right eyebrow as if he were waving good-bye to someone in slow motion. It was the first time Torres had been in the presence of a Vietnamese field officer.

"Sergeant Torres, hello. I am Thiuta Thang. I am glad you are here. Where in America are you from?"

"I am from Puerto Rico, sir. I have been in the army for seventeen years, but this is my first tour of duty in your country. I am married and have two daughters. I'll try to teach your soldiers what I know and help in anyway that I can," Torres stated to the officer.

"I will see you later and sometime we can have dinner together with the others. When we go in to the field, we have a security squad to watch out for you. We don't want anything to happen to you, okay?" the major said.

"Thank you, sir."

"Okay, Sergeant Torres, go back and join the others in the bunker. I have to talk to Thiuta about a forthcoming operation. I'll see you later," the captain said.

Once again Torres saluted. He walked out of the command bunker and headed for the advisory team's bunker. On his way back, he passed a young lieutenant. The officer stopped and said, "Chao, Thuong Si Nhut. You are the new Co-Van. I am Lieutenant Thiem and I speak some English. I will be your interpreter when you go out to the field and any other time you need me."

Torres saluted him and said, "Chao, Lieutenant Thiem. I am learning very fast and with people like you it is easy."

"I am from North Vietnam. My family came to the south because the communists did not like Christians. My family is Protestant and we are Christians. I speak the language of North Vietnam, which is a little different in pronunciation from that of the south. I graduated from the officers' academy. Some people in the battalion do not like me. It is okay. They may be jealous, but I do not care. I do not think Thiuta likes me, but he needs me because I speak good English. Better than anyone in the unit."

The captain came out of the bunker where he had been conferring with the major. When he saw Torres talking to Lieutenant Thiem, he said, "I see you've met Lieutenant Thiem already. He speaks good English. He's a good man. He likes to work with us. He probably told you where he comes from and that his family is Christian. He may become a first lieutenant very soon. Isn't that right, Thiem?"

"Oh, I do not know. Some people do not like me."

"You will make it to lieutenant. Don't worry. Come, Sergeant Torres, I want to give you more information. Good-bye, Lieutenant Thiem."

After saying good-bye, the young officer walked away.

"Thiem is alright," the captain told Torres. "You'll like him. He comes with us when we're out in the field and interprets for us. When we meet people at the villages, he is needed. We want to communicate with the locals, and he is our voice."

The two men walked into the bunker and the captain continued to brief Torres. "For meals, you can eat whatever you want to. Sometimes Thiuta invites us to eat with the Vietnamese officers. You can pay them for the food if you want. We each give about twenty dollars in Vietnamese money, which is ample. An old soldier named Thiep is the major's cook. He can cook for you also. For the most part, we eat C rations, but if you do want to cook, there is a stove. There's only one burner, but it works. We also have all kinds of heating tablets. Can you cook?"

"Captain, my mother taught me and I've learned a lot from my wife. I cook many Spanish dishes and you'll like them. I'll make some pasteles. They're like tamales. There are a lot of green bananas here and green leaves to wrap them in."

"Gunny here can cook all kinds of Western foods. You'll be eating a lot of rice if you eat with them."

As Torres sat down on an empty chair and began to memorize code signals, the captain said, "Sergeant Torres, your personal code will be Bronco Four. I am Bronco One, the lieutenant is Bronco Two, and Gunny is Bronco Three."

Torres's first night at the outpost passed without incident. There were some rockets and machine guns firing in the southeast. He could see a plane well known by the nickname "Spooky" firing its rockets and guns toward suspected enemy positions. Torres walked around the perimeter of the outpost and talked to some Vietnamese soldiers who were positioned around the hill. Flares were being fired from various positions. The outpost had four howitzers in position, and once in a while the soldiers fired a sortie. The buzz of radios, static, and messages being sent as well as received could be heard distinctly as the darkest of the night was setting in.

Torres's radio watch was from 2400 hours to 0300. He was asked by the captain before the watch list was set up, "Sarge, what time would you like to keep watch tonight? It's up to you. We each take three hours, beginning at 1800 hours and ending at 0600 hours."

"Give me the watch from 2400 to 0300 hours. I want to accustom myself to being awake late at night, although I don't think it will be too much of a problem. I wake up very quickly when I hear shots being fired or someone calling me," Torres said to the officer.

Torres's radio watch went by without incident, and as he'd been instructed, he radioed his reports on time to higher headquarters.

9

The next day Torres was instructed to get ready and accompany Gunny Tim to Tam-Ky. The captain called Torres, saying, "Sarge, I know it's your first full day here, but the quicker you get familiarized with everything around here the better it will be for you. Keep the equipment that you need. The rest, pack in your duffel bag and take back with you. We have a storage area at the Vietnamese compound back in Tam-Ky. Gunny has a key and you'll get another. We keep rations stored there also. Bring some back with you. Gunny will show you where District Headquarters is and also other important places you may need to go to sometimes in the future. Familiarize yourself with the roads and the MACV compound in Tam-Ky."

Torres answered, "Yes, sir. I'm ready to go. It's best for me and I appreciate it, Captain."

Torres secured his weapon and mounted the jeep, which Gunny Tim already had ready. Private Hoi was seated in the rear seat. Gunny said, "It is 0900 hours and the road to Tam-Ky is already clear. The security platoon clears it every morning. They check for mines and booby traps and also for any possible ambush by guerilla forces. Let's go now and we'll have time to go to Chulai. I may see some friends there that I'll introduce to you. They help us with food and equipment once in a while."

On the way, Torres noted some straw houses near the road and farmers working in rice paddies. Some were planting rice and others were harvesting it. Water buffalo were grazing, and some women were carrying poles across their shoulders with baskets or straw buckets hanging from each end. There were many children in view. Banana plants were near each of the huts.

Just before reaching the west end of town, the men in the vehicle noted a cemetery. Some women standing behind a group of men carrying a coffin wrapped with a South Vietnamese flag were crying. Among those carrying the coffin were some military personnel.

Hoi said, "Co-Van, the man who is dead was a marine and those women are part of his family. The lady with the black piece of cloth around her shoulders was his wife. Maybe the mother and sisters or daughters are there also. Someone gets buried here every day. You can see the marks of the tombs," Hoi concluded while the jeep continued on toward the city, which was only about two hundred yards away.

Driving the jeep through a narrow street, Gunny Tim came to a stop in front of a small hut where a barber was cutting hair. A sign above the door indicated it was a barbershop. There was a small, short stairway and on the top wooden step was a young girl about nine years old with a baby boy about three in her lap.

Torres could not conceal his curiosity and watched as she checked the baby's head for lice, taking the parasites in her mouth and biting on them before spitting them out. Torres was repulsed but also pitied the girl's ignorance about health measures. He took a quick glance at Hoi, and the young soldier shrugged his shoulders as if to say that was the way things were here for some.

Gunny Tim said to Hoi, "Hoi, you stay here and go to the Vietnamese compound. It's not too far. We'll pick you up at the storage building when Torres and I get back. We're going to Chulai and then the MACV compound. We'll pick you up at 1400 hours. Do you understand?"

"Yes, Gunny Tim," Hoi answered.

Hoi jumped off the vehicle and walked away, while Gunny Tim drove south along Route 1 toward Chulai Marine Base. The trip took about an hour. Just before reaching the marine base, Gunny passed through a narrow gate, and on a signal by a lone marine guard, he drove into a small compound surrounded by barbed wire and concertina wires. The camp did not have more than ten canvas squad tents, which served as quarters for a Marine engineering unit.

Gunny stopped the vehicle in front of one of the tents marked as the mess area and, stepping quickly out of the jeep, summoned Torres to accompany him outside. "Come with me, Torres. I want to introduce you to some good people."

"Sure," answered Torres, entering the tent behind Gunny Tim. Inside, Gunny Tim introduced Torres to a marine sergeant first class, who had a tag on the right upper pocket of his fatigues identifying him as Sergeant Stephens, mess sergeant.

"Hello there, Stephens," Gunny Tim said. "I want you to meet Torres. He's new with the team, but I know that you'll help him if he comes around. He may get you some AK 47s or other weapons when we go in the field, which will be very soon."

"Glad to know you, Torres. Just come around whenever you have time. I'll take care of you. If you need any C rations or class A food, like steaks or porkchops, I can give you some. It's better than eating the Vietnamese food like dog, chicken guts, or raw fish," Sergeant Stephens said to Torres.

"Well, I'm glad to know you also. Thanks a lot for the help. I'll see what I can do for you," Torres said.

"What do you need, Tim?" the mess sergeant asked then. "I have some juicy steaks; I can give you at least twenty. I don't have chops. I have canned corned beef, potatoes, and plums, which are good for your digestive system if you intend to spread the rice paddies with your human waste after you eat five or six steaks. The farmers may give you a medal for fertilizing their fields. With your build you could cover at least a couple of acres."

"Come on, Stephens. I'm not that big of a manure head."

All three laughed.

Sergeant Stephens walked toward some cardboard boxes and began packing some food into an empty one. He closed the cardboard box and carried it to Gunny Tim. "Here, take this. I know you have to go now. Take care of yourselves, both of you. I'd like to see you later."

Gunny Tim and Torres thanked the mess sergeant and, after loading the rations into the backseat of the jeep, they drove out of the compound.

"Torres, do you need to buy anything from the base exchange" Tim asked. "I can drive you to the main base and you can buy whatever you need."

"No, I think I have everything I need for now," Torres answered back.

"Well, in that case, let's go back to Tam-Ky. We'll stop at the MACV compound and have a beer with the Aussies. They work with us also and they're a helluva bunch of good guys. You'll meet some of them. There may be some fellows you may know there also. The compound sergeant in charge is named Castro, and I think he's Filipino. He has a Spanish last name like yours. He may speak Spanish and you can chatter with him. He's a nice fellow," Gunny said, while he continued driving the jeep in a northerly direction.

About forty minutes later, the two men came into the southern outskirts of Tam-Ky. Just before entering the city line, Gunny Tim drove ninety degrees to the right. Two hundred yards ahead the vehicle came to a gate. Two marines with patches on their left shoulders indicating they were security guards were standing watch. One of the guards had a tag with the name Garza on it. He was a private first class. Recognizing Gunny Tim, he greeted him.

"Hello, Gunny. When can I go into the field with you? Let me know when your battalion is going to a field operation; I want to get my combat badge. I can as soon as my platoon sergeant says he'll let me go. I know. He told me already last week. I want to go with your team.

"Hey, you have a new member. I see your name is Spanish—Torres. I'm PFC Garza, and I speak Spanish. I'm from Texas. You're Puerto Rican, aren't you?"

"Glad to know you, Garza. Yes. I just arrived yesterday, and Gunny is taking me on a tour. You'll be welcome with the team, I'm sure."

"Thanks, Sergeant Torres. I'm ready to go anytime. I get bored here, and I want to see some action. I know how to take care of myself."

Torres said, "I'll see you later."

Gunny Tim said, "We must go to the Australian Club and have a drink now before we head back to the hill." He proceeded immediately to drive toward the club, which was located at the far northern end of the compound.

When the vehicle stopped in front of a wooden barracks, Torres stepped out. Following Tim, he walked in through the building's front door. Inside there were long tables where some officers and noncommissioned officers from the Australian Army were talking and drinking Australian beer out of the can. An officer named McKenzie walked toward Tim and said, "God save the American Indian. Hello, Gunny. How are you? Who's your friend? A new member of your team?"

Gunny answered, "Chief, this is Sergeant Torres; he just arrived yesterday. God save the Queen and all the kangaroos until you get back and hunt some of them. You know, Torres, I'll bet you the chief eats kangaroo meat."

"Two beers for the warriors of the 4th Battalion. Da Co-Vans. I'll pay," said the chief warrant officer.

"Thanks," said Torres and Tim, while the chief gave them both a beer and introduced them to the others, who happily shook hands calling out their names and ranks.

Gunny said, "Well I must go on to the operations room, Chief. You may be having to take my place very soon. I'm going on R and R and I have to check to see if my request has been approved.

"Let's go, Torres. We also have to pick up Hoi and the supplies at the Vietnamese compound. We can't waste any more time. Thanks for the beers."

Both men walked out of the club and headed for the operations room, which was a short distance away. Gunny walked in and asked the clerk, who was seated behind his desk, "Hey, buddy. Are my orders for R and R approved?"

"Sure they are," the clerk replied. "You'll be leaving in the middle of this month."

While the clerk was speaking, a sergeant first class walked out of the NCOIC room and said, "I knew I heard a familiar voice. Hello, Tim. Hello, Torres. Remember me?"

"Sure, Castro, I remember you," Torres replied.

Both men had been together in Hawaii while Torres was stationed at Schofield Barracks serving with the 14th Infantry Regiment, which was nicknamed "the Golden Dragons" and was attached to the 25th Infantry Division. They also had known each other at Fort Dix.

"You'll get your orders, Gunny. Get in here about five days prior to the orders going into effect. That will give you enough time to be in Saigon and depart on your leave. Now, take care of yourself. You too, Torres. I'll see you around sometime. I have to go check the area," Castro said, walking out the door.

"Let's go, Torres. Hoi must be waiting. We don't want to drive up the hill very late," said Gunny.

Gunny and Torres got in the jeep and drove off toward the northern edge of the city. Gunny Tim briefed Torres along the way. After driving a short distance away from the city, he drove west along a dirt road and came to a halt in front of a huge camp surrounded by barbed wire and high towers, dispersed with a distance of about two hundred yards between them. They were sandbagged around, and no guards were visible in any of them. The gate was open and a movable barbed wire barricade had been pulled aside, which allowed the vehicles to drive in without delay.

Gunny stopped for a few minutes and said to Torres, "That big building over there is District Headquarters. To the left is the operations center. They control prisoners of war and also handle operations of the paramilitary forces. To the right is Operation Headquarters for Australian forces assisting the military operations here. To the rear of the district is the prisoner of war compound. There are quite a few prisoners in there, thousands actually. To the rear of the Aussie operations building is the district jail and directly to the north of it is a staging area with zinc buildings with cement floors. There are a few small hamlets around, mostly located to the north and west along the high ridges."

"Thanks, Gunny, for the information. It's good to know all these places. I may have to visit them sometime."

Gunny drove the jeep inside the compound and came to a stop next to wooden building about twenty feet in length and ten feet wide. He stepped out and, pulling a key from his pocket, proceeded to unlock a padlock attached to the front door.

"I don't see Hoi, but I know him. He'll be here as soon as I ask about him from any mamasan around here. He'll show up immediately. Let's get some C rations first, and then I'll do that."

The two men entered the room, Torres carrying his duffel bag, along with the equipment he was going to leave in storage. They loaded a couple cases of C rations into the back of the jeep. Then Hoi came out of a hut, which was almost directly in front of the storage building.

"Here you are," Gunny said. "Are you ready to go?"

"I'd like to stay, but I don't want to be punished. Thiuta will get mad and order me to shave my head."

"Well, let's mount up and get out of here," Gunny said.

The three men got in the jeep and headed for high ground, following the same route that they had taken earlier. After they reached the top of the hill, one of the security sergeants came to pick up the jeep and drive it back to the Vietnamese compound they had just left, where he would secure it until it would be needed once more by the advisory team.

As Torres's second night on the hill came around and twilight was closing in, he walked around the perimeter and met some members of the battalion. They were very friendly and smiled at Torres, as one of them said to him, "Thuong Si Nhut, Da Co-Van Moi." This meant, "The sergeant first class is the new advisor."

"Da," Torres answered ("Yes").

Torres approached a machine-gun position that was covering the perimeter defense area facing the east toward Tam-Ky. There was a Vietnamese sergeant standing by with a semiautomatic carbine in his hands. The moon was very bright and full. It was like a huge round cheese, and the sergeant was looking at it as if he wanted to fly up to it.

Torres walked back to the advisory team's bunker. Just as he was about to enter it, he heard a burst of shooting coming from the location where the Vietnamese sergeant had been standing. Torres turned back to check out what was going on and saw some Vietnamese soldiers running toward the location, where a man was lying on his back.

The battalion commander, along with some officers and others, came out of their bunkers and approached the area where the body was. Captain Johnson and the lieutenant came out to check out what was going on also. The operations sergeant came toward Captain Johnson and informed him that a Vietnamese sergeant had tried to kill himself and was badly wounded. Sergeant Torres said, "Let's call Dust-Off," meaning the evacuation helicopter.

The major walked by as if he was already aware of what had happened and said to Captain Johnson, "No Dust-Off. Let him die. He wanted it that way, poor fool. I told him what to do this morning, and he didn't do it. He deserves to die."

"Okay, Thiuta," the captain answered.

Torres wondered what was happening and what the major had meant by his words. Seeing Lieutenant Thiem, he walked up to him and asked, "Lieutenant Thiem, what does the major mean when he says the sergeant deserves to die?"

"Co-Van, you do not understand, but I will tell you now. The sergeant had a wife who lived in the village down this hill facing north; he and his wife had two baby boys. All of them lived together. The sergeant found out that his wife is no good and she is not loyal to him. She loves another sergeant from another battalion. Thiuta told the sergeant to go to the village and kill his wife and the other man, but instead he killed himself. Apparently he felt shamed. That is why the major said he deserved to die."

Torres said, "Thank you, Lieutenant. But what a shame! Maybe he loved her too much and that's why he did it. It's hard, but I hope the two boys are okay. If they get to grow up, they'll never understand.

"This also happened back home. I remember when I was twelve years old and an uncle of mine killed a man. He was a good man and my uncle was also. Both were friends, and while they were playing dominoes one night they argued. They were having some drinks. When my uncle returned back home he was drunk and told his wife about the argument he'd had. He then got his revolver and went to shoot the other man. My uncle went to the man's home early in the morning. When he heard the banging at his door, the innocent man came out. Not knowing he was going to be shot, he opened the door to greet my uncle and instead got killed. When my uncle came to his senses, it was too late. He separated from his wife after spending ten years in jail. He was sentenced to twenty, but they paroled him."

"Co-Van, we find people like that everywhere. Good night. I will see you soon," the lieutenant said as he walked toward his bunker.

Torres said, "Good night, Lieutenant. I'll see you, sir."

Torres walked back to his bunker. The night passed without any further incident.

10

At 1000 hours the next day, Captain Johnson called the team together. "I'm going to give you some information about a forthcoming operation that may occur in the next eight to ten days. The major is going to a briefing today and I'll be going also. Gunny, you are going on R and R and a replacement will be sent from headquarters to join us. If the operation starts in less than eight days, you'll be going with us. Your leave will start after we come back. The operation may not last more than five days. Any questions?"

No one said a word and the captain walked out of the bunker and climbed aboard a Huey helicopter that had landed at the site and was waiting for him. The chopper flew away immediately after the captain got aboard. Lieutenant McDuffie would remain in charge while the captain was away.

Torres started to assist in the marksmanship training of the battalion. He walked down the hill and at an improvised rifle range he taught and advised the soldiers in using the marksmanship technique known as "quick kill." It was a technique in which a soldier or rifleman engaged the enemy quickly by pointing their weapon and firing it without using the aiming sights. Torres had graduated from a course while he was at Fort Knox, Kentucky, where experts from Fort Benning, Georgia, had come to administer the course at the Armor Center.

The Vietnamese soldiers and commanders were very pleased with the technique and immediately talked about the importance of training everyone in it.

Captain Johnson returned to the OP two days later and immediately called the team in for a quick briefing.

"We'll depart in two days; the operation may last for five. Gunny Tim, you'll go with us. You'll leave on your R and R after we return. I'll have more information about the operation very soon, after I speak to the battalion commander. Are there any questions."

No one said anything.

"Well, since there are no questions, that's all I have to say for now."

Two days later everything was in order and ready. The unit started to move in a northerly direction, following the ridges of the high hills located to the west of the city of Tam-Ky. They reached the first hamlet, which was almost at the northern edge of the OP. The reconnaissance platoon had cleared the way ahead of time.

The battalion adopted a wedge formation. A rifle company moved in behind the reconnaissance platoon, and the other two rifle companies took a flank each. They were slightly to the rear of the leading company. Supporting and headquarters elements were located to the rear of the leading company and almost in line with the flanking companies. A security platoon was guarding the rear in order to prevent any surprise attack from that direction.

When the headquarters command approached the hamlet, no adults could be seen around. There were not many children, but a few were standing by the huts where they probably lived. They looked apprehensive and shy. It was the first time Torres had sensed a feeling of despair among the young he saw. He remembered an old poem he'd read once called "The Three Wise Men," in which it spoke of the sufferings of the young ones and how the three wise men wouldn't stop and give the children presents because of the war. Christmas was only a couple of weeks away.

Torres could not help noticing two young boys huddling and clinging to each other. They were about three to five years old. They were standing by the semiopen door of a hut; it apparently was their home. Torres stopped suddenly, and Lieutenant Thiem walked over and asked, "What happened, Co-Van? Anything wrong?"

Torres replied, "Sir, I just want to give some candy to the kids. Will you help me communicate with them? Tell them not to be afraid, please."

The lieutenant immediately answered, "Sure, Co-Van. Why not? Come with me. I will talk to them."

Torres followed the officer, who walked up to the door where the two kids were huddled together. In Vietnamese he told them not to be afraid and accept whatever Da Co-Van gave them. The kids apparently understood.

Torres dropped his pack and immediately opened a strap from a side pocket. He pulled out some small bags of M&M chocolates and handed them to the boys, who reached out apprehensively with their tiny hands. After they grasped the bags, they held them against their chests. They smiled and as a gesture of thanks lowered their heads. The lieutenant said, "You know, Co-Van, they appreciate your kindness. Now we must go. We have to keep moving."

The two men walked away. Following the trail, both hurried to catch up with the rest of the staff. As they walked, the lieutenant sidled up to Torres and said, "Co-Van, I want you to know something about those two boys. Remember the sergeant who killed himself? Those two kids are the sons of that sergeant. You had only been at the hill two days when it happened. Now they don't have a father. I hope someone takes care of them. Maybe their mother is inside the house," the lieutenant concluded.

Torres said, "I hope someone takes care of them, as you said. I thought about them being the kids of the sergeant. It's very sad."

Both men caught up with the staff.

The unit continued to move along the trail, which was wide enough to accommodate a cart like the ones used by the farmers to carry their harvested rice home or to market. At the end of the trail an extensive rice plantation came into view. It was divided by multiple paddies, each separated by dirt banks or wide ditches. Some of the ditches were full of running water, and their banks were very slippery. The men had to jump over them in order to prevent getting wet. Some could not jump far enough, what with the weight of their packs and other equipment; they slid back into the water and had to be helped out.

As evening was approaching, the units in front and to the flanks cleared some areas that were suspected of being hideouts for the enemy. No hostile action had been encountered yet.

The staff reached the outskirts of a wooded area, where some banana plants and breadfruit trees were growing. There was a wide ditch and Lieutenant McDuffie tried to jump across. He failed to reach the other side and slid into the ditch. He twisted an ankle and came out limping. Torres noticed and immediately asked, "Are you okay, sir? Do you need any help?"

McDuffie replied, "Don't worry. I'm okay. I'll make it." He slowed his pace and at times walked very haltingly.

As the unit entered the wooded area, they came in sight of a village, where some concrete buildings and a very well-preserved pagoda were standing. One of the buildings was marked with a huge board above the front door, indicating it was a school.

The battalion commander ordered the unit to stop and camp for the night. The village chief came out and met the staff. He was accompanied by some of the elders, and they greeted everyone in a friendly way.

The advisory team members had hammocks made of nylon cloth. They followed the staff security and hung each hammock from trees that were conveniently separated. Everyone dug foxholes directly under their hammocks. It was very convenient in case of emergency; all they had to do was roll over and drop into the holes. The battalion commander stayed in a house with members of the operations staff.

The night went by without incident. No report of friendly casualties was received and only sporadic firing of small arms weapons could be heard.

When the staff was ready, they had breakfast, which was a can of C rations. Using heating tablets, the advisory team warmed some instant coffee and drank it.

About 0800 hours the staff assembled in front of the school where the schoolteacher was greeting the students, who ranged from five to ten years in age. He lined them up in front of the school. The battalion commander approached the teacher and asked him some questions, which he answered in a very polite manner. Captain Johnson walked up to the major and asked if he could take some pictures of the school and of the kids.

"Thiuta, can the teacher get the kids together and let us get some pictures?"

"I don't see why not," he answered. He walked up to the teacher and after relaying the captain's request, the teacher immediately obliged. He moved the kids and aligned them by height, with the smallest in front. The captain decided to sit with them, and Torres also did the same. Some members of the staff joined the group. The captain started to give candy to the kids and they each thanked him. Torres also gave candy to some of the children. It was a very happy moment.

The unit continued to move north. Some sporadic firing of small arms was heard from the advancing direction, giving them the impression that contact had been made by the reconnaissance elements moving ahead. The movement was slowed at times by hours and at times some artillery explosions were heard.

It was the second day of the operation and no major contact had been made with the enemy. Again the unit halted as night was approaching. The headquarters staff camped at a small hamlet. The huts were dispersed, and the banana and breadfruit trees offered a natural camouflage to the hamlet as well as to the people living there. There were many dirty embankments and piles of dirt around the huts. Green grass, taro roots, banana plants, and sugar-cane stalks covered some of the mounds around them. There were also a few tropical trees of varied species.

The area had supposedly been checked by the reconnaissance and security elements before being occupied by the staff. Gunny Tim and Torres hung their hammocks, using the same tree for one of the ropes of their hammocks. There was an embankment to the north of their position. It was about ten feet from the hammocks, and it could provide natural protection from any ground fire coming from that direction.

The captain and the lieutenant were about twenty-five meters to the northeast and not clearly in sight of Gunny Tim and Torres. A Vietnamese soldier carrying one of the advisory team's radios was near Gunny Tim and Torres.

The night was very calm and only flares requested by the artillery units were fired at intervals of thirty to forty minutes. Radio watch for the advisory team was set, and Torres had the midnight hours. Reports were relayed until 2100 hours. Radio silence was maintained until 0500 hours the next morning.

The Vietnamese radio carrier for the team noticed that something was moving and that the dirt had been disturbed at a mound to the north of his position. He walked over and began sticking the bayonet of his rifle into the sides of the embankment. Almost at the same time, the sound of loud booms from grenades was heard.

Gunny Tim ran off in the general direction the noise had come from. Torres stayed and secured his equipment. The young Vietnamese uncovered the top of the mound he had jabbed and out came two guerrillas with their hands and arms up in surrender. There were hand grenades inside their position, and it would have been possible for them to throw one of the explosives at Tim's and Torres's positions and blow them to pieces. The guerrillas probably thought they were going to get captured or killed if they exposed their position.

Torres walked over and caught up with Gunny Tim. Both men continued up a trail in the direction of the explosions, which had now ceased. They heard some noise and loud talk in Vietnamese. A sergeant was giving commands to someone inside a partially destroyed bunker to come out immediately with his hands up.

A young woman about thirty years old, dressed in black, came out of the bunker, crying and sobbing and asking for mercy. She was also trying to help a man who had apparently been badly wounded in the head and chest. He was bleeding profusely and was almost unconscious. The Vietnamese sergeant asked the lady, "Are there any more inside?"

The woman replied, "Yes, but maybe they are dead. My husband is hurt. Please help him. We are not Vietcong. We were hiding from you because we thought you were going to kill us. We did not hurt anyone. There are no Vietcong in this village."

The sergeant said, "You lie. You are Vietcong and so is your husband."

The woman continued to cry, and the Vietnamese sergeant ordered the two young soldiers to carry the wounded man out and make a hammock to move him away.

The battalion commander, who had been standing nearby watching what has going on, told the sergeant to accompany the soldiers while they brought the suspected Vietcong back. The sergeant took the young soldiers' rifles, while the two men raised the hammock by lifting the poles at either end and placing them on their shoulders. The woman took a rag and tied it around her husband's head to try to stop the bleeding.

As the two young soldiers carried the wounded man back, his wife clung with her right hand to the right of the hammock and grasped the edge of the cloth near her husband's head. She was crying and trembling, showing apprehension for the condition in which her husband was.

The group was joined by a young corporal who, on command from the sergeant in charge, took the two rifles from the sergeant and slung them over his shoulder. Meanwhile, Torres had walked back to check the area where his hammock was hanging. He intended to fill the hole he had dug under it.

When he walked back, he heard some screaming and loud sobbing coming from a nearby area. He immediately said to Gunny Tim, "Let's check out what's going on."

He walked up to a small hill behind some taro bushes and saw the sergeant in charge of the detail that was carrying the wounded man. The two soldiers had laid the hammock down on the ground, and the woman was hysterically begging for mercy. The sergeant had his weapon pointed at her head in a very menacing way and was yelling at her.

Torres immediately walked over and placed himself in front of the muzzle of the sergeant's weapon, saying loudly, "Khong Khiet" ("Don't fire"). The sergeant dropped the muzzle of his rifle and said to Torres, "Khong Khiet, Co-Van."

The two soldiers picked up the hammock and continued to walk down the trail to the east, where rice paddies lay alongside the trail. The corporal accompanied them. Lieutenant Thiem came over and asked Torres, "What happened, Co-Van?"

Torres said, "Sir, I hope the sergeant takes the wounded man and his wife back safely. He almost killed the woman. It's not right; she should be treated properly as any prisoner of war should be."

"Yes, I know, Co-Van."

Torres had joined Gunny Tim and was talking to him about the incident when they heard two shots coming from the general direction of the rice paddies. Torres walked back up the small hill. At a distance he saw two bodies lifeless in the middle of the rice paddy. He knew they were the man and his wife. They were no more than three yards apart from each other. The sergeant and the soldiers who were carrying the hammock were not in sight. The corporal was walking back in Torres's direction, and Lieutenant Thiem, who had come over also to check out what had happened, asked the corporal in Vietnamese, "Cai gi do?" ("What is the matter?"). The soldier answered, "Chung no su trong" ("They escaped").

Torres asked the lieutenant what had happened. He said, "He says that they tried to escape and wouldn't stop. They had to shoot them."

Torres said, "I don't believe it, Lieutenant. The man was almost dead, and his wife was not going to run away from her dying husband."

The lieutenant said, "I will tell Thiuta about it."

"It is not good, sir," Torres said, shaking his head, as he realized that the same thing had probably happened many times and would happen again and again.

Torres walked up to Gunny Tim and, in a very somber mood, said once more to himself, but loud enough to be heard by Gunny, "It's not right. They should respect the rules of the Geneva Convention."

Gunny immediately asked, "What's the matter, Torres?"

"Gunny, I just saw something very bad. A defenseless woman and her husband were killed. The two people who were pulled out of the bunker, remember?"

Gunny said, "Well, what can we do?"

Torres said, "We should play it safe, but I don't like things like that to happen. Maybe Thiuta ordered it when the sergeant was told to move them back. The lieutenant said he's going to tell him about it."

Torres and Tim rejoined the staff, which was about ready to continue to move up north and on to the next village.

"You know, Gunny, I heard from other advisors back in the States that in some units like this one about forty percent of the soldiers are Vietcong sympathizers. Sometimes I wonder about it. Maybe they're tired of fighting or maybe they witnessed some bad treatment toward people. Those could be some reasons."

"I don't know, Torres. It could be that they don't want to fight anymore."

"They told me too that I should sleep with one eye open at all times," said Torres.

"Well, Torres, up to now nothing has happened to any of us in this battalion, and I hope our luck continues."

"We'd better not even think about it, Gunny."

Lieutenant Thiem walked up to Torres. "Co-Van, I think you will make many friends here as well as enemies, but there will be more friends than enemies. It's better to make more friends because then your enemies can't touch you. Maybe later you will understand why. You'll see."

"Thanks a lot, sir, for the warning. I do really appreciate what you just told me. Thanks for the advice, my friend."

The unit continued to move across rice paddies and some men checked in between wooded areas for any hiding guerrillas.

11

The battalion commander received the order that the operation had been terminated and they could return back to the blocking position they had occupied before the action started. The operation had lasted only three days, and reports of friendly casualties were negative; no one from the battalion had been hurt. The battalion reported that the enemy had suffered about twenty dead and some wounded; few were listed as captured.

The unit came up to a very wide-open area, and the commander gave the order to move east toward Route 1. When Route 1 came into view, vehicles to carry the soldiers back were waiting, lined up to the right of the highway. They were facing south toward Tam-Ky. The advisory team's jeeps were waiting, the battalion commander's vehicle in the lead.

The quarter-ton trucks were brought up by some members of the security platoon. The men were loaded into the two-and-a-half-ton trucks, and on the command of the battalion commander, the convoy started south. Gunny Tim was driving one jeep and Torres was in the passenger's seat. Private First Class Hoi was riding in the back seat and next to him was a chubby, young soldier nicknamed Boom-Boom. They were going along as security. The captain was riding with Lieutenant McDuffie, who was the driver; in the back was Lieutenant Thiem and a sergeant named Fong, who was a member of the reconnaissance platoon.

Two hours later they reached the outskirts of Tam-Ky. There Captain Johnson received orders that another operation was to start soon. He stopped by the Tam-Ky compound to be briefed. Gunny Tim, along with Torres, went to Tam-Ky MACV Compound to check his leave orders and also to pick up a replacement while he was away.

They entered the MACV compound and parked the vehicle in front of the orderly room, where they were met again by Sergeant First Class Castro, who was the acting compound commander or first sergeant. Torres walked around and to his surprise saw an old friend he had known, who had also been at MATA School in Fort Bragg.

"Hello, Buddy. How are you? How did you get here? I thought you were still with the 4th Corps. How is Hicks? Did you get assigned to the same team?"

"Torres, I just got here not knowing where I was going. They assigned me to the 1st Battalion of the 2nd Regiment. I put in for my transfer and it didn't take long to get it approved. Well, anyway, I'm here."

"But tell me, have you seen Hicks? How is he?"

"Torres, remember how he used to say that he was going to end the war in seven days. Sorry, pal, but I have to tell you he was killed two days ago. Sorry, my friend. That's why in war soldiers should never become close friends with anyone."

Torres pulled a handkerchief out and openly wiped his eyes, saying, "You're right. It's sad. Maybe when he said he was going to end the war he was predicting his own death. I hope his soul rests in peace. I hope his family will understand and find consolation. Well, what else can I say?"

"I know, Torres. It's bad to lose a friend. By the way, I also saw another of our school partners. Remember Oshiro?"

"Sure, I remember him, Melendez. Nice fellow. Where did you see him?"

"He just arrived yesterday at Quang Ngai. He was assigned to an armored battalion as advisor. You may see him sometime."

"Take care of yourself, Melendez. I have to go and look for

my friend; he's checking his R and R orders and also his temporary replacement. Good luck and keep your head down."

"Good luck to you too, Torres. Be careful."

Torres walked back to the orderly room. "Where did Gunny Tim go?" he asked the clerk.

"He went to pick up Chief Warrant Officer McKenzie at the Australian Club. He's to be Gunny's replacement for the time he's on R and R. He told me to tell you to go out there and look for him. Do you know where it is?"

"Yes, I do. Thanks for the information. I'll go now and check on them."

Torres walked out of the room and headed for the Australian Club. He walked in and Tim was drinking a beer.

"Hey, Torres, I see you're looking very sad. It's not because I'm going on leave, is it? I'll be back, pal. Here is Chief Mack. He'll be with you while I'm gone."

"Hello, Chief. How are you?"

Torres extended his hand after saluting McKenzie in a military way; then he said, "No, Gunny. I just got word that a friend of mine was killed at the Delta. He was a very good friend, and I can't help thinking how happy he used to be. He said he was going to end the war in seven days and that's all he lasted. Well, I'll just say a prayer for him."

"I'm sorry, Torres, for your friend," said Gunny.

"Me, too," the chief said. "Here, have a beer," and the chief handed Torres a Black Label.

"Thanks, Chief," said Torres.

"Well, now it's time to go up the hill. Are you ready, Chief?"

"Yes, I am. Let me get my pack. It's over in the corner there."

"I'll help you carry it, Chief."

"Okay, thank you, Torres."

The two men went to pick up the equipment, and Gunny walked out of the club and headed toward where the vehicle was parked. The two men behind got to the jeep, and after loading the equipment in the back, Torres jumped into the rear seat and Chief McKenzie sat in the passenger seat. Gunny Tim started the vehicle and, after backing it for a short distance, he drove ahead and left the compound.

They arrived at the OP at almost the same time a chopper was landing at the pad. A young man carrying a radio on his back unloaded a duffel bag and jumped off. He moved over to a safe area away from the flying Huey, which immediately took off and continued its flight. Captain Johnson, who'd already arrived with the lieutenant, went over to meet him.

"You're Private First Class Crane, the forward observer? You'll accompany us on our next mission. Stick with our team when we go out. We'll look out for you. Come, I'll assign you a bunk. You can help us pull radio watch while we're here. I want you to meet the other guys."

"Thank you, sir," Crane stated, picking up his gear and following the captain to the advisors' bunker.

As soon as the captain walked inside the bunker, followed by Crane, he stated, "This is Crane. He'll be with us as forward observer in case we need artillery support from the big guns. He's with the American Division. He'll stay as long as we need him.

"The mission, as far as I know, is to locate some 122 rocket launchers that the enemy has up in the hills to our west. These rockets have been used to hit Chulai and also some have hit the Tam-Ky area. I'll give you more information when I get called for another briefing and have all the facts.

"Gunny, you'll go with us; then you can go on your R and R. Tomorrow you can go and pick up a young Marine security guard at the MACV compound. He'll be going with us; his boss gave him permission."

"I know who he is. Torres met him the other day. His name is Garza. He wants to get his combat badge. Torres and he speak the same language."

"Hey, Gunny. He seems to be a nice fellow. He's of Mexican descent and from Texas. I may practice my Spanish with him," Torres said.

The captain stated, "Chief McKenzie does not have to go. Maybe next time Gunny goes on leave the chief will come with us."

Early the next day Tim drove to the MACV compound and brought with him PFC Garza. He also brought a dozen rat traps.

"Guess what, Torres? Remember that television series 'The Rat Patrol'? Tonight it will come back into action. I have some salami and twelve rat traps. Let's see how many we can get."

"Okay, Tim. The ones you arm to that side there, you take care of. The ones on this side, I'll take care of." Torres pointed to the west and east respectively.

"Okay, pal. We'll see who gets the most. If I get more, you cook them and eat them. If you get more, I'll share my part with the rest of the team and bring some to the Montagnards up in the hills. They eat them, you know."

"I'll give all of mine to them, and you can have some if you want," Torres said.

Gunny replied, "Believe me, I'd eat a rat if I were hungry and didn't have any food. We eat pork chops and pigs eat garbage. Put a chicken in a roach party and it will clean them up. Rats eat only corn, grass, and some insects; they eat cheese and good meat." He continued arming the traps.

It was almost 1700 hours when the sound of a snap broke the silence inside the bunker.

"Click! I think I got one, Torres! The first one."

The husky marine pulled a trap next to his bunk and everyone looked at a rat, who was still twisting its tail.

"Oh! This bastard weighs about two pounds. Look at those teeth."

Suddenly another click was heard from Torres's side.

"I think we're even now, Gunny."

It was exciting as the night went on; almost no one could sleep. The traps were snapping about every fifteen minutes. By the morning the rat count was thirty-eight KIA rats. Gunny took them and aligned them outside, and the Vietnamese soldiers came over to check them.

"Number one, Gunny," said Hoi.

"Yes, Hoi. Many rats. Maybe soldiers here do the same and put traps in their positions. They can catch some, too. When we finish inside the bunker, we'll give the traps to them."

For two nights the traps clicked at a rate of one every thirty to forty-five minutes. The total count was sixty-eight dead rats.

Captain Johnson called the team together. "Tomorrow we'll depart on a search-and-destroy operation to get the rockets. Get ready today. Be sure you have everything you need before we depart; we may be out for a week. Are there any questions? Okay, that's it, men.

"Gunny, I'm sorry you have to go, but we'll be okay, and when we come back you can have your leave."

"Alright, Captain. I don't mind. It's been fun catching rats in here for the few last days. I think I may catch a snake. I think there's one by the entrance to the bunker, hiding between the sandbags."

"No kidding, Gunny? You'd better catch it before it gets one of us. It probably came out because the rats are scarce now around here," said Torres.

"Yes, Torres. I know how to get them. You'll see."

Two hours later Tim shouted, "Come here, Torres, everybody. Look what I got. It's about five feet long. I'll get Sergeant Fong, and he'll help me cut its fangs."

Sergeant Fong, who'd heard what was going on, walked in and joined the group. "Okay, Gunny. I'll hold the snake and you cut its teeth."

Gunny pulled out a sharp jungle knife and cut the inside of the snake's mouth, while Fong held the snake. The reptile twisted and curled around Fong's arms. "Now, let's get some pictures before it dies. Torres, go and get a camera."

"Okay, Tim. Jungle Tim in action. The tamer of snakes and the number one rat killer. What did you do in the war, Daddy? That's probably what your kids will ask you. What will you say?"

Torres went inside the bunker and brought out a small camera he had been carrying inside his pack.

"This is nothing, Torres. This is going to be our lunch. Have you ever eaten a snake sandwich? Well, get ready because you're about to eat your first one."

"I'll eat it after you take a bite first. I ate frog legs once in a restaurant in New Jersey. I was on the way back home from Korea. It tasted like chicken to me. I imagine snake will taste like fish."

"You're right, pal. Let's get a picture of you and the snake. Wrap it around your neck. Lieutenant, come here. Get hold of it and act natural. It won't hurt; the fangs are out."

Gunny finished his photo snapping, took the snake over and skinned it, and prepared his gourmet dish. Torres took a piece and made himself a sandwich. Gunny ate almost all of it. Some of the other guys took a bite too.

The next day the unit started to move down the hill at about 0700 hours. The direction of movement was west, toward the high hills. At the beginning the movement was slow in anticipation of preventing any possible ambush by the enemy. The famous Vietcong 48th Battalion and some North Vietnamese Army forces had been reported as being active around the area. Rain was expected to fall during the next five days.

The first day they did not engage the enemy. The unit moved across swampy areas where snakes and leeches measuring up to eight or ten inches in length were swarming in streams and water puddles. Some booby traps had been found and properly detonated by the reconnaissance elements moving in front.

The second day there was no change and no contact or reports of friendly or enemy casualties. No rockets had been located. The unit moved in between ravines and climbed well above four thousand feet. In some areas the jungle was very dense, and in others there was only elephant grass growing.

On the third day the skies opened, and it started to rain hard. The rainfall started about 1100 hours and by 1500 hours there had been almost four inches. It stopped long enough to give some of the soldiers time to smoke a dry cigarette or to squeeze out their wet clothes.

About 1800 hours the order came from the battalion commander to stop and set up security for the night. At 1900 hours flashes and booming sounds were heard and observed to the north. There were rockets being fired from launchers at a distance of almost three thousand yards. Because visibility was poor due to the humidity and the terrain, they could not initially determine if the rockets were being fired in the direction of the battalion. Reports came in from Tam-Ky that some rockets had landed to the south of the city and north of Chulai. Only eight rockets had been observed being launched.

It started to rain once more, and it did not cease throughout the night until almost 0500 hours. The commander, on orders, had sent the approximate location of the rockets and the air force was to deliver an air strike. At 0700 hours the B52s delivered their cargo. From the ground Torres could see the jet streams high up in the air, after hearing the crack of the detonations as the bombs hit the ground.

Thiuta received the order to terminate his forward movement or to check on the results of the B52s' bombing. A reconnaissance plane flew over the area of the suspected rocket-launcher positions.

Heading back, the battalion moved at a fast pace, following

the same route they had walked earlier. Torres told PFC Garza, "You got your badge, although we didn't make any ground contact. We have to be careful because there may be booby traps along the trail going back. I really don't know why the unit is following the same path back."

Suddenly a big detonation was heard from the front about four hundred yards ahead. A booby trap had been set up and two soldiers from the reconnaissance elements were the first casualties. They had been killed and two others were wounded.

The unit slowed its pace and at about 1500 hours it was already within one thousand feet of the OP. The commander ordered the men to stop and regroup. The humidity in the air had caused many of the soldiers to sweat heavily. The advisory group assembled in a small area, and Torres, as well as the others, unhooked their packs from their backs. Torres sat on the ground and leaned back on his pack, which was resting next to a horned cactus. The cactus looked similar to a pineapple plant. Garza was standing up and, in a very low tone of voice, he said to Torres, "Sarge, don't move. Don't even breathe loud. When I tell you to jump, do it quick as a flash. Do you get the message? Don't move."

Torres, realizing that Garza was not fooling around, stayed very calm and waiting for his word.

"Now," Garza yelled. At the same time Torres threw his body forward in a fast motion. He looked back at the cactus and saw a green viper snake resting on a leaf of the plant not more than twelve inches from where his left ear had been. Garza immediately hit the leaf with a stick. The snake disappeared, crawling under roots of the plant.

Torres, very grateful to Garza, said, "You just saved my life. If I'd have moved one inch, that snake probably would have bitten me. I'll never forget this. More than ever I have to be grateful to you. This is the second time by chance that a Mexican has done something for me. Viva la Virgen de la Guadalupe! Viva Mejico! Thank you, friend."

"That's okay, Sarge. You probably would have done the same thing for me or anyone else."

"You deserve more than the badge you're going to get. I'll see you around the compound sometime, Garza."

The unit got the word to move, and in about twenty minutes, the advisory group was already resting in their bunker. Garza and Crane returned back to their units just as the courier chopper came to deliver the team's mail. Both young men thanked the team for their support, and the team also thanked them back for theirs.

Torres walked up to PFC Garza and shook hands, "I'll see you, my friend. Take care and good luck, Garza," he said to the young marine.

12

Captain Johnson assembled the team and said, "Tomorrow, Sergeant Torres and Gunny will go to Tam-Ky. Gunny, you can stay for a few days at the compound until you go on R and R. Sergeant Torres, you can bring Chief McKenzie back with you. Hoi and Boom-Boom will accompany you as security. You don't have to bring Hoi and Boom-Boom back; they'll find their own way."

The next day Gunny and Torres were ready to depart by 1000 hours after the road had been cleared.

Hoi and a young, chubby, short Vietnamese soldier came to meet Gunny and Torres, who were standing by the vehicle ready to mount it. Gunny asked, "Are you ready, Hoi? Is your friend ready also?"

"Yes, Gunny, we're going with you and we're ready."

Both young soldiers climbed in the rear seat of the jeep. Torres and Gunny climbed in after the marine sergeant's equipment had been loaded into a trailer attached to the jeep.

As they rode down the hill, Gunny said to Torres, "Before we stop at the MACV compound, we'll drop Hoi and Boom-Boom off at the Vietnamese compound; then we'll drive to Chu-lai and see my friend at a small camp outside the base. Remember Sergeant Stephens, the mess sergeant?"

"Sure I do, Gunny."

"I'm going to check with him to see if he wants me to get something for him when I go on R and R. We won't stay long. I may need something from the base exchange; if you need anything, you can get it too."

"Alright with me, Gunny," said Torres.

Torres turned around to the rear seat and asked, "Hoi, I know what the words *boom boom* mean to you and the people here, but why do you call your friend here Boom-Boom?"

Hoi laughed and the chubby young soldier also joined in with a guffaw when he learned that Torres was asking about his nickname.

"Co-Van Torres, Boom-Boom here likes all the girls. He makes love to many of them. He is same as American lover boy. He got beaucoup girls in Tam-Ky and many villages."

"In other words, you mean he is papasan to many babysans?"

"Yes, he is papasan to beaucoup babysans."

The young soldier said, "No, no babysan. Me like boom-boom. No babysans."

"In America we would call him a stud. Like a big bull. A horny guy."

The men laughed as the vehicle reached Route 1 and the center of Tam-Ky. They headed for the Vietnamese compound. As the two young soldiers got out of the vehicle, Gunny said, "Now, Hoi, you go and make some mamasan happy, and you, Boom-boom, do the same with the girls. I'll see you when I return. Have a good time."

"Good-bye. Chao, Gunny."

Both young soldiers said good-by as Gunny and Torres continued their journey toward Chulai.

"Gunny, Boom-Boom reminds me of Sancho Panza, the sidekick to Don Quixote. He is a miniature Sancho Panza. I hope Hoi doesn't get in trouble with a jealous husband if it's true that he comes here to chase mamasans."

"Torres, Hoi is very smart and knows better than that. He knows what he's doing."

"When they see those guys both coming their way the people around the compound and Tam-Ky say, 'Watch out! Close the doors and lock up the girls! Boom-Boom and Hoi are in town! The dynamic studs!'"

They laughed as they continued south along Route 1. When the marine spotted some small villages along the road, he said, "Torres, you see those girls standing by the front doors to those hutches?"

"Yes I do, Gunny."

"Well, those girls are prostitutes looking for money from the GIs who pass by here and sometimes leave the camps looking for a short time."

The jeep slowed as they passed through these built-up areas, and Torres and Gunny could hear the girls saying almost the same words, "Short time. Five dollars, GI. Come over. Stop here."

Some of the girls were dressed western-style, their lipstick and rouged cheeks unevenly applied.

"Torres, kids running around have been born to some of these women. They'll never know their fathers."

"I saw that in Korea, Gunny. It's the same in other places. I hope they'll be okay after the war, if they survive it."

"The bad thing also is the venereal diseases some of these girls carry," stated Tim.

The men arrived at the same small camp where Sergeant Stephens was working as mess sergeant. Sergeant Stephens walked out of the mess tent and, recognizing Torres and Gunny Tim, said, "Here you are again. Anything I can help you with, fellows?"

"No, Steve. Torres and I came over to check if you want me to bring you anything back from the other side. I'm going on R and R, and I thought maybe you would want something."

"I thought you already went on R and R."

"No, Steve. I went on a field operation. I'm going now. Torres came with me and he'll drive back with my replacement, an

118

Aussie named Chief McKenzie. You probably know him."

"No, Gunny, I don't know him. If you care for something, let me know before you leave."

"By the way, Steve, I saw a broken-down Army jeep up there." He pointed to a quarter-ton truck that was resting on the side of the trash cans near a small hill. "What's the story with it?"

"Some Army unit was here before and left it behind. It needs some mechanical repair and new tires. It may run. Something like that would not be wasted at home."

"Nobody cares about it and it may go to the disposal area at Chulai. If anybody needs it, they can have it."

"I see what I may do when I come back from R and R. Right now, Torres and I have to go. We're off to the base exchange to buy some stuff I need before I leave on R and R."

"Good luck, Tim. And you, Torres. Take care of yourselves. Don't feel sad because the chief in here is going on the warpath on the other side. He'll come back."

"Don't worry, Steve," said Torres.

"Torres, I have some peaches. If you want some cans, you can have them," said Stephens.

"Sure. They may come in handy and I do like them."

The sergeant went inside the tent, brought out a case of canned peaches, and loaded it into the backseat of the vehicle.

"Thanks, Sergeant."

The two departed, waved good-bye to the mess sergeant, and continued on to Chulai Base Exchange, where Torres bought some candy and Gunny Tim secured some toilet equipment he needed. As they left the base, Torres decided to ask Gunny Tim, "Can you stop at the souvenir store?"

"Yes, Torres. Are you going to buy something?"

"As a matter of fact, I will. I want to buy a shoulder holster for me and another for a police friend of my uncle's in my hometown. His name is Baez and he's a sergeant in the Police Department. I promised to get him something."

"Okay, Torres."

Gunny Tim stopped the vehicle a short ways from the front gate of Chulai Airbase and Torres asked the storekeeper, who was a Korean, to show him two holsters. After paying for them in Vietnamese money, he climbed back into the vehicle, first placing his old holster in the back of the vehicle and exchanging it for one of the others he had just purchased.

They got to the MACV compound after being signaled many times by the girls standing by the hootches still offering the same goods. "Hey GI. Short time. Come here. Five dollars. Boom boom. Me number one."

Gunny did not slow down even once during the trip. When the entered the compound, Gunny stopped the vehicle in front of the orderly room and walked in. Seconds later he walked out of the front door accompanied by Acting First Sergeant Castro, who immediately recognized Torres and said, "Hello, Torres. Why don't you go on R and R with your pal here? You can be his bodyguard. He may need one when he goes on the warpath."

Torres said, "I just got here and besides, I think Gunny can take care of himself."

"Tell him, Torres."

"Well, Gunny, I hope you don't do anything I wouldn't do. Look, that's your room over there. It's ready for you." Castro pointed to a room located to the right of where they were standing.

"It's room 15. You can stay there as long as you want until you leave on R and R. Anything you might need just go and check with the supply sergeant or come see me. We'll get the word to you when you'll be leaving on your R and R. Any questions?"

"Oh, everything is fine, Buddy," Gunny said.

"Well, I'm leaving you now, Gunny. I must go and look for the chief."

"Torres, he's waiting to be picked up at the club. He told me

120

to tell you that he's ready to go. Just go up there and you'll find him with his buddies."

"Alright, Castro. I'll go and check now. Good luck, Gunny. I'll be seeing you. Don't hurry back. Enjoy, and take your time." Torres walked toward the Aussie Club, while Gunny said, "Take care, Torres. I'll see you when I get back, Buddy."

Torres waved his right arm toward Gunny and continued walking toward the club. Castro helped Gunny with his bags; then he went away to check the area as he usually did.

Torres entered the front door of the club and the chief, who was sitting to the right of a long table with some of his friends, greeted him with his British accent.

"Welcome, Torres. Is everything okay? Gunny Tim, is he ready to go on R and R?"

"Sure, I just left him. He's in room 15," said Torres.

"How was the last operation?"

"We lost a couple of guys and two more were wounded. Booby traps got them."

"What a shame! Torres, these are some of my friends. They fly planes and choppers." The chief pointed around the table where some soldiers were sitting drinking beers and eating snacks. Torres walked around and shook hands with all of them.

"Have a beer, Torres, before we go. If you need something to eat, help yourself," he added, pointing to a bar where some cold salads and other items had been placed.

"Thank you, Chief. You guys are very hospitable. Were you in Korea during the war, Chief?"

"As a matter of fact, I was."

"I was there also, serving with the 3rd Infantry Division. Did you ever go to a town called Uijonbu?"

"Yes, there was a club there for our troops to relax and have a drink. Were you there?"

"I was one of the guys selected to go and see Bob Hope when he brought over his show for the troops. He brought Marilyn Monroe, big-nosed Jimmy Durante, and a beautiful young blonde girl who was married to the actor John Hall. It was a great show and I enjoyed it.

"Well, anyway, I visited the club that you fellows had and right above the wall facing the entrance was a huge picture of the queen of England. Beautiful picture. There were Australians, British, and Canadians sitting around enjoying their drinks. Someone somewhere said something bad about the queen. That was it! I didn't even have a chance to get my beer. There were bodies, glasses, chairs, tables, and everything else you could think of flying all over. It was a real riot. I walked out untouched. I don't know how that happened! The Royal Military Police, with the help of the American Military Police, came over, about a platoon of them. It took them quite a while to quell the riot; I'll never forget it. Hey, Chief, were you in that fight?"

"I don't know, Torres. I was in so many that I still have the bruises. But I enjoyed them."

"Chief, I'll never say anything against Her Majesty myself, and if I'm ever with a British, Canadian, or Australian citizen and hear any of them say something bad about the queen, I'll split."

"I don't blame you, Torres."

"Well, we'd better go now before night; otherwise the captain will worry, Chief."

"Yeah, let's go. My pack is ready. I'll see you soon, my friends. Keep the beer cold and stock up for my return."

The guys around the table stood up and, almost at the same time, said, "Good-bye, Chief. Good-bye, Torres. Take care."

As Torres drove the vehicle back, both men continued to talk on diverse subjects, including their tour of duty in Korea during that war.

The next day, after a quiet night, Torres stepped out of the bunker and walked around the hill's perimeter. It was about 1000 hours when he saw a young man at a distance and thought he recognized him. Sergeant Fong passed by Torres, who called to him, "Sergeant Fong, that soldier over there looks like Hoi, but his head is shaved. Is that Hoi?"

"Yes, Co-Van. That is Hoi and he feels ashamed. That's why he doesn't come this way."

"Why did he have his head shaved?"

"Well, Co-Van, he and Boom-Boom took the other jeep after you dropped them off at the compound yesterday and went around to look for girls. The Vietnamese Military Police arrested and reported them. Thiuta ordered the heads of Hoi and Boom-Boom shaved. He did not put Hoi in jail because he works with co-vans and you need him. He speaks more English than the other soldiers. But Boom-Boom, besides getting his head shaved, is in jail for five days."

"Poor Boom-Boom. No girls for five days. That may kill him. What jail is he in? Maybe there are girls with him," Torres said.

"No way, Co-Van. If you go around that bunker you'll see him."

Torres walked slowly and carefully toward the bunker. Prudently he spied a small corral with barbed wire stretched around and over it at a height of no more than two feet from the ground. Torres could see Boom-Boom kneeling down; he resembled a miniature Buddha. There was an empty tin plate in front of and to the right of a tin cup of water. Torres did not want to be noticed by Boom-Boom as he felt the young soldier would feel more ashamed. Poor Boom-Boom wouldn't even be able to stand up for the next five days.

Torres walked back and asked Sergeant Fong, "If it rains, will Boom-Boom have to stay in there?"

"Night and day, rain or shine, he must complete his punishment. But do not worry, Co-Van. Boom-Boom has been there many times before. He knows how to live. He'll come out and

123

he'll do other things. He likes to do number ten things (the Vietnamese, Korean, and Japanese soldiers refer to 1 as a good thing and 10 as a bad thing). Thiuta has punished him many times. He just loves to go boom boom, boom boom; that is why people call him that. If they locked him in there with a girl, he would never want to come out."

Torres felt sad for Boom-Boom, but he could not abstain from laughing a bit at the remarks made by the sergeant.

"I'll see you, Sergeant. Thanks for the information."

Torres walked back to the bunker as the sergeant, walking away, replied, "You are welcome, Co-Van."

The captain left two days later for headquarters, as usual to get information about the next scheduled operation. When he returned, he informed the team that an operation was due to start in about three days and that the area of the operation would be west of the city of Song Tin. The mission was to clear out some strongholds that were thought to be occupied by local guerrillas. The location of the strongholds varied from villages to the high grounds northwest of Tam-Ky. There would be a forward observer in case artillery support was needed. The captain would join the team a day before departure. The operation was to last until the area was cleared; no time limit was given.

13

Three days later the unit moved by truck, following Route 1 in a northerly direction. Just before they reached the city of Song Tin, the men were ordered to dismount and move west. Once more they assumed a wedge formation. Crossing rice paddies immediately adjoining Route 1, they reached some low ridges and ravines descending from hills about one thousand feet in height. On the way, the battalion encountered sporadic sniper fire and also destroyed some booby traps.

The reconnaissance platoon searched some hootches in which farmers lived with their families. The people were questioned as to enemy whereabouts and activities. The hootches were scattered and generally everyone had a water well for their use. Some also had one or two water buffalo, a few pigs, and chickens. Clearly some farmers had a higher standard of living than others. Some houses had cement floors instead of plain dirt. There were some with concrete walls, tiled floors, and two or more rooms.

A squad of one of the rifle companies, which was moving not too far ahead of the staff group, approached a lone straw house and searched it. Outside there was only a young girl about nine years old tending and feeding a small groaning and squealing pig that had become very excited by the presence of so many strangers. The girl was feeding some grass and green banana peels to the agitated animal. The girl also showed signs of tension and nervousness.

The leader of the squad walked up to the girl, saying something that was unintelligible to Torres. The girl apparently did not understand what the sergeant had said and did not answer. Suddenly Torres heard a shot, in combination with others, some distance ahead. He also heard the sharp squeal of a mortally wounded animal. Following a brief silence, the girl began sobbing in desperation as she looked with tenderness and grave concern at her dead pig. The sergeant had shot the animal and had immediately called two young soldiers and a corporal and ordered them to carry the lifeless animal back to be prepared as their meal.

Torres walked over to the area and saw the sergeant pointing his rifle at the head of the girl in a menacing way, threatening her. She did not even look up. Torres ran up to the sergeant and stepped in front of the weapon, which was aimed in a somewhat oblique direction toward the ground. At the same time he shouted, "Khong kit" ("Don't fire").

The young girl, apparently running out of tears, continued to sob in an attitude of resignation and despair, waiting for her death also. She did not even notice Torres, who had taken off his pack. The sergeant walked away.

Apparently a member of the staff had seen some of what had happened and had gone to notify the staff. The operations sergeant came over and summoned the sergeant, the corporal, and the two soldiers who had carried the pig away. The commander ordered the operations sergeant to collect money from the squad members and pay the young girl for the pig. Sergeant Bam, the operations sergeant, collected the money then kneeled down and placed it in the girl's right hand. Lieutenant Thiem came over. Torres walked up to him and said, "Number ten."

"Yes, Co-Van, number ten."

Torres took out some candy and, in a very somber mood, walked over to the girl, kneeled down beside her, and said, "Ni ghia Co." He handed the candy to her, which she grasped. Innocently lifting up her head, she showed the marks of dried tears.

The lieutenant said to the girl, "Thank the Co-Van, lady."

The girl said, "Cam on Ong."

Torres replied, "Khong ci gi!" ("You are welcome"). He stood up and the girl walked inside her hootch, holding the candy and the money in her hands. Torres once more said, "Chao, Co," as the girl entered the hootch's front door.

The lieutenant, walking away from the area with Torres at his side, said, "Co-Van, I know what you said to the girl when you gave her the candy. I still say, Co-Van, you are making many friends and enemies, but the friends will be more. Next time when you say to a girl that she is beautiful, you probably will get a smile from her. I know you told her she was a beautiful girl."

Torres replied, "Sir, I hope that next time it happens, as you said, it will not be under the same circumstances."

"I hope," the lieutenant answered.

They continued and joined the staff. Torres could not stop thinking about what he'd witnessed. He wished things did not have to be like that, and he hoped that such atrocities would come to an end soon.

The unit came to an area where coconut palms were abundant. There were embankments in which the coconut, royal, and chestnut palms were aligned like soldiers in parade formation. Torres said to Chief McKenzie, "I hope no snipers are hiding out as the Japanese did in the Pacific and as I have seen in movies."

"No, I don't think so, Torres. The guerrillas don't take those kinds of chances unless they have the upper hand."

"I hope you're right, Chief."

The staff stopped in a sporadically wooded area, and everyone got ready to warm up some rations for their meal. It was in the late afternoon. Torres and the staff were close to the edge of a wooded area and a rice plantation that separated it from the dense forest area ahead of them.

Torres walked over to the edge of the wooded area and looked straight ahead at the dense jungle, not showing proper concern for his own safety. The battalion commander saw Torres and immediately sent Sergeant Fong over. In a very agitated tone he said, "Co-Van, move back to the concealment area. There are many snipers in the forest up there. The major sent me over to tell you."

"Thank you, Sergeant. I appreciate it."

Minutes later shots were heard and word came to the staff that some units were receiving sniper fire from the wooded and dense forest to the front. A soldier had been slightly wounded in the arm, but he was in fair condition.

The unit rested for the night after a search party was dispatched to find the snipers. No contact was made, and a perimeter defense was established.

The next day the unit started once more to move along the high and low ridges, searching for guerrilla forces. At noontime Torres saw a soldier carrying a young puppy under his arm. The staff cook, named Thiep, was a corporal and he was more of a personal cook for the battalion commander than anything else. He was the oldest member of the battalion and had been a soldier with the Vietminh forces in the struggle against the French. Hoi, who was standing next to Torres, said, "Co-Van, do you like Vietnamese food?"

"I don't know, Hoi. I haven't eaten much of it except for bananas, breadfruit, and the other vegetables that you grow here. We grow and eat the same at home. I like rice. Back home we eat it almost every day."

"It is number one. Maybe you like other food. Corporal Tiep makes number one food with meat."

Torres looked at the soldier walking with Hasi Tiep, who was dragging the puppy by a rope attached to its neck. The dog did not want to cooperate. The soldier walked back, reached for the animal, and held it under his left arm. The men continued their march until they stopped by some hootches. It was noontime and they were to stop for some time in the area.

128

Torres sat under a breadfruit tree that had large fruit hanging from the stems. They were different from the ones he had seen at home. He asked Hoi, "Hoi, these fruits are different from the ones I see at home. How do you eat them?"

"Well, they are good to eat when they are ripe. In Tet we eat them. They are number one. They have a taste like a banana and the papaya fruit. You will like them. When Tet comes, I'll get some for you. In parties we eat it."

"I like mangoes. Are there mangoes here also?"

"Yes. When we go to Hue you will see many there."

The young soldier, whose hair had grown back in a bit, walked over to where Hasi Tiep was preparing the battalion commander's meal. Torres, with curiosity, saw the young soldier in the distance with a dead animal in his hands, trying to conceal it from the others' view. Blood was dripping on the ground. Torres could only make out the tail of the dead animal, but he knew it was the puppy. He realized that it was going to be the commander's lunch.

Thirty minutes later, as the team was resting and some of them were about ready to eat, Lieutenant McDuffie stood up and said, "Well, I'm going to eat now. The major invited me. I'm going to have *khong cho*."

"Hum," Torres said. "I think I've heard that word before when I first arrived in Saigon. It was at the dental clinic and the dentist said it. What is it, Captain Johnson?"

"It's dog."

"That's what I thought. The lieutenant must like it. I won't eat it. Back home we have two beautiful dogs and they are like family."

"If the major invites you, you don't have to eat it."

"I know, but I'll tell him in a diplomatic way that I don't have anything against them eating it. I'll excuse myself and tell them that back home we consider dogs pets, and we love to have them in the family."

"That's good, Torres. And in case they ask you about how much money you make, you can tell them you only get $75 and you don't know how much money your family gets at home. The officers here make less money than an American sergeant."

"Thanks for the tip, Captain."

Minutes later, the lieutenant returned, licking his lips. "It was good!"

Torres glanced at the chief, and, in a low tone, said, "I wish it would bark in his guts."

"What?" the chief asked.

Torres, with an indifferent attitude, said, "Nothing, nothing, Chief."

"Hum," the chief rebuffed him.

The unit received word to get ready to move again. They were slowed down by the terrain and their search for some dugout positions that proved to have been abandoned recently by the Vietcong. The sound of small firearms and hand grenade detonations came from the front.

The leading reconnaissance elements were ambushed by a small Vietcong force. A corporal who was leading the party was killed, along with two more soldiers. His name was Nguyen and he was the one most trusted by the battalion commander and the operations staff. He was well liked by the members of the battalion, and he was a well-decorated soldier. AK 47 automatic fire from a concealed position had cut the three men down before they could get cover.

The staff moved up to the location where the ambush had taken place after the contact with the enemy was broken and all was clear. The guerrilla forces had left two dead men behind. The ambush site was well concealed as the positions of the dugouts could not be clearly distinguished under the patches of guava bushes that were spread all around. The unit got the order from the battalion commander to continue on the mission.

On the fifth day, the unit moved from high ground to a valley, which, as usual, was planted with rice. It was harvest time. The staff stopped by two houses that were not more than four hundred yards apart. Curious, Torres walked close to the house located to the north and nearest the direction of the staff's marching orders.

Torres noticed that there was a corral attached to the extreme right of the house. A huge, black water buffalo was standing calmly and placidly braying. Torres drew near the corral and at the same time looked up at the front yard of the house. A young girl, about twelve years old, was standing there. She had a twelve-foot pole in her hand. At the opposite end of the pole was a tin bucket. Another water buffalo was yoked to a long pole that was extended horizontally from a wheel secured by a vertical pole no taller than the buffalo. The vertical pole was buried in the ground. There were dry rice stalks that had been harvested aligned to the sides. The buffalo walked around and around like a merry-go-round pony. As it went, moving clockwise and stepping over the dried rice leaves, the hoofs of the animal caused the rice grains to come loose from the spikes. It was a tedious job.

Torres glanced toward the chief and said, "I'm glad I'm not a water buffalo."

"Me, too," stated the chief as he walked away.

Torres felt very calm and at ease while he continued to watch the young girl with a pole in her hands. He did not want to guess but thought that maybe she collected the loose rice after the buffalo had walked around and detached it from the spikes.

"Ruff, ruff, ruff, ruff." There was a loud braying followed by many more and a sound like a stampede coming toward him. Torres jumped up, his heart beating like it was the end of the world and a huge train was going to run over him. He ran up to where the chief was standing.

"What's the matter, Torres?" the chief asked.

Torres held his breath, calmed down, and looked toward the

corral. He glanced around to see if there were any trees he could climb easily in case he had to.

The operations sergeant came over to Torres and said, "Co-Van, don't worry; it won't get out. Water buffalo don't like the smell of strangers. If an American gets too close to one of them, they become very mad."

The chief started to laugh, and Torres, looking at him, said, "It's not funny, Chief. That beast almost got out of the corral. What would *you* do? Would you stay and face it? I'm not a bullfighter."

The chief could not refrain from laughing and immediately said, "You're Spanish; just get yourself a cape and face it like a man. We'll be shouting, 'Olé, Torres.'"

"Olé, my butt. You go in there, Chief."

Torres glanced around again at the corral and at the other yoked buffalo, who still kept going around and around.

"Sergeant, you said those beasts don't like my smell. I don't smell that bad, do I?"

"No, Co-Van, it's anyone who is not Vietnamese."

"I didn't know you had prejudiced water buffalo. Somebody should have told me that before."

"It may kill you if you get close."

"Not me. I've learned my lesson. Once I was chased by a wild boar in Germany and I climbed a tree. I'll jump on top of you or even the major or the captain if I have to."

The chief looked at Torres and, walking away and still laughing, said, "Olé, olé, and olé, Torres."

Torres could not contain himself and laughed too; then he said, "Bull, bull, and bull."

Curiosity once more got the better of Torres, and he looked again at the young girl with the pole. She had not done anything with it yet. She was still holding it. Suddenly the yoked water buffalo came to a stop and assumed a position like a huge crawling worm curving itself to take a giant step forward. The young girl ran up, but away from the rice leaves and loose grain. Torres knew immediately that the beast was ready to relieve itself and drop manure over the grain. The girl quickly extended the pole with a bucket at the end and placed it behind the beast's hind legs. He almost filled the bucket with manure while the girl steadily held it, although the basket and the pole were very shaky from the weight of the waste.

Torres looked at Lieutenant Thiem, who had just come up to him, and asked, "Sir, if that girl drops the bucket or doesn't get there on time, what happens?"

"Co-Van, the girl must wash the rice, and she may get punished."

"What a job! I hope she grows up and gets to marry some good guy."

"You don't know, Co-Van? She is going to be married very soon. That water buffalo was given to her father as a present. Sometime this week the man who will marry her is coming with his father to fetch her and take her home. She will become part of the family in the other house."

"Sir, I respect your culture, but I hope someday things like this will change. She is so young, just a baby."

"It is like that, Co-Van, but I know what you mean."

"Thank you, Lieutenant."

Torres walked up the chief and, mumbling, said, "Chief, I have two daughters and no Cadillacs or Mercedes Benz will ever be exchanged for them."

"What are you talking about, Torres?"

"Do you know that the girl has been exchanged for a water buffalo?"

"No."

"Well, she's engaged, and she probably doesn't even know who is going to be her husband. I hope at least he's a good fellow."

"I hope," the chief said.

"Back home kids complain when they're asked to go to the corner store. How lucky they are, Chief," Torres said.

14

The battalion returned to the blocking position and the staff came back to the observation post, which had been occupied for the time it took to complete field operations. It had been almost ten days since Gunny Tim left. He was already on the way back, and Torres thought that very soon he would probably have to go and pick Gunny Tim up at the Tam-Ky MACV Compound. There was not much time and only four weeks before Christmas.

"Torres, I want you to go and pick up Gunny. He's back."

"Alright, Captain. When do you want me to go?"

"Tomorrow. He just got back today. We may move south to Quang Ngai province. It's also an area of operations for the Americal Division. You can get some supplies from storage when you pick up Gunny."

"Yes, sir."

The next day Torres, the chief, and Hoi departed for Tam-Ky. The chief had completed his mission as Gunny's replacement for the time he was absent.

Torres drove to District Headquarters after dropping Hoi off at the Vietnamese compound and instructing him to wait until he got back with Gunny Tim. The Australian Operations Center, which was very near District Headquarters, was located behind the political prison.

"Torres, drop me off at the operations center. I can get a ride there to the compound," said the chief.

"Okay with me, Chief."

As Torres drove the short way, he saw two sergeants walking by the American Counterintelligence Center, which was located near District Headquarters and to the south of the Australian Operations Center.

"Hello, Logan. How are you?" Torres recognized one of the sergeants and greeted him.

"Hi, Torres. How are things with you? I knew you were with the 4th Battalion."

"It's been fine up to now. Is everything going okay for you?"

"Yeah. I just heard that the Vietcong may release some prisoners as a gesture of good faith, propaganda, or the Christmas spirit. The rumor is they are two Spanish fellows who were captured a long time ago. One is supposed to be a marine and the other an Army guy. Those are the rumors. You know how it is."

"Well, I hope whoever they are, regardless of what the purpose may be, get released. As long as we get them back, it's okay with me. Thanks for the information. I'll see you fellows. I have to turn Chief McKenzie loose at the Australian Operations Center."

"Good luck, Torres, and you too, Chief."

"Take care, guys," the chief said.

Torres drove up and the chief dismounted from the vehicle. Unloading his equipment, he said, "I'll see you, buffalo fighter."

"Good luck to you too, kangaroo tamer."

With smiles on their faces, they went their separate ways.

Torres arrived at the MACV compound and entered the orderly room. "I came to pick up Gunny if he's back."

"Torres, thank the Good Lord you're here," said Castro, who stood up from his desk.

"What's the matter?" asked Torres.

"What's the matter?" said Castro.

"Yeah, is anything wrong?" Torres asked.

"Anything wrong? You ask? Listen, that Indian you came to

pick up went on the warpath last night. He got tipsy and apparently it was too much for him. I don't know how, but he got hold of a radio, called an artillery unit, gave them our coordinates, and requested an artillery barrage. He had a map, too. Luckily the fellow who got the message thought that something was wrong, and in verifying the coordinates found out that it was this location! You'd better take him out of here before he kills all of us."

Torres laughed, "Gunny did that? Look, Castro, I had a companion in Germany. His name was Lightfoot and every time he got drunk during the winter and while it was snowing, he'd stick his right arm out of the window of the room we shared. It was before my old lady got to join me, and I was sleeping in the barracks. Once I felt the draft and I was freezing my butt off. I got up and saw he had snow piled on his arm. He'd kept it outside for almost thirty minutes. I got him to close the window and finally go to bed. The next day he couldn't remember a damned thing. I told him he should change his name to Cold Ass."

"They sure can't hold any liquor. I'll come with you to be sure he goes. Up there, there's nothing to drink and he can't get drunk."

Both men walked to Room 15, where Tim was packing and almost ready to go.

"Hello, Gunny, welcome back. Are you ready to leave?"

"I am not, but I have to go."

"You'd better be ready or we'll have to move the compound."

"What do you mean, Castro?"

"Don't you remember anything about last night?"

"I know I found a radio and came to bed a little warm."

"You mean drunk. With guys like you, we may not even have to fight the VC. They may even thank you and give you a medal."

"My head hurts."

Torres started to laugh out loud.

"What are you laughing about, Torres? My head hurts. Please, when you drive back, don't try to hit any potholes."

"Good-bye, Gunny. Good-bye, Torres. Take your time, Gunny. Just get back here after I'm gone. I don't have too much time to go. Only a couple of months." Castro walked away and started to check the area.

Torres and Gunny left the compound and drove to the Vietnamese compound to pick up rations at the storage building. He also picked up Hoi and all three men returned to the observation post.

Two days later Gunny and the lieutenant went back to Tam-Ky. They wanted to get their hair cut. Torres went with them. The captain was at headquarters, getting information on the forthcoming operations since Christmas was drawing near. Torres was to stay at the storage room for the night and get clean laundry and other necessities. The captain allowed the members of the team to take a break away from the OP once in a while.

The lieutenant and Gunny returned. The captain also returned with his replacement, since he was about to be promoted to major. Lieutenant McDuffie was also on the list to be promoted to captain. He would be taking over as senior advisor of the team in a couple of months. A second lieutenant named Gatlin was to join the team as the newest permanent member. He was also a Native American like Gunny Tim.

After Gunny Tim dropped Torres at the Vietnamese compound, he departed with Lieutenant McDuffie. Torres rested for a couple of hours at the storage room; then he decided to walk to District Headquarters.

A vehicle came by and Sergeant Logan waved at Torres.

"Hey, Torres, did you get the word?"

"About what?"

"The VC released two guys this morning. They're two Puerto Ricans like you. One is named Agosto, the other Rivera.

Rivera is an Army specialist four and Agosto is a Marine PFC. They've got them at the CID Operations Center. They're debriefing them now. You may be able to see them and also talk to them. The building is about two hundred yards to the left; you'll see the sign."

"Thanks for the information, Logan. I'll be seeing you."

"Good-bye, Torres."

The vehicle drove away and Torres kept going toward the CID building and District Headquarters.

When he reached the area, he saw a sign that read COUNTERINTELLIGENCE SECTION—U.S. ARMY. He glanced through and saw a young Hispanic man sitting on a wooden chair. He was dressed in Vietnamese clothes similar to light yellow pajamas. Torres walked up the stairs and said to him, "Hola, como estas? Muy contento en verte. Mi nombre es Torres y soy consejero militar aqui en esta area."

"Estoy contento. Nos soltaron esta manana. Soy puertoriqueno y mi companero tambien. Lo estan interrogando ahora."

"Una vez mas, me alegro de verte. Buena suerte."

The conversation had been brief. "Hello, how are you? I'm happy to see you. My name is Torres, and I'm a military advisor in this area."

The soldier had responded, "I'm happy. They released us this morning. I'm Puerto Rican and so is my buddy. They're interrogating him now."

Torres had said, "Once more, I'm happy to see you. Good luck."

Both men shook hands and Torres walked out of the building with the feeling that the news was going to bring happiness to many people back home, especially the families of the two young men. He did not even care about the fact that he had not asked the man's name; he just felt happy for them. Very shortly they would be on their way home, and that's what mattered.

Torres passed District Headquarters and continued to the southern part of the two-story cement building. He was trying to make a visual reconnaissance of the area. There were some U.S. Army trailers parked along the road, which extended from north to south directly behind the District Headquarters Building. Up to the north there was also a huge fenced-in area, with buildings all around to the left of the road.

The fenced compound also had turrets, with automatic gun emplacements and two guards each managing them. It was the district prisoner of war compound. Approximately eight thousand to ten thousand prisoners were held there. Directly to the front of the POW compound was another compound that was the political prisoners compound. It was smaller than the other, and there were cells around it. The cells all had steel doors. There were supposed to be about thirty hard-core cadre lodged in them as prisoners. Women were also part of the prisoner contingency. There was only one prisoner per cell in the political prison.

Torres continued his walk and, turning south on the road, he came to some houses made of straw with cement floors. He looked down a short, wide, dirt trail and saw a middle-aged Vietnamese gentleman walking up to the door of one of the hootches. The man was dressed like a Catholic priest from his waist up.

Torres glanced through the opened door of the hootch and saw an altar with a figure of Christ on the cross. There were candles lit to the left and right of the altar. Torres said to the priest, "Toi muon cau-nguyen Chua" ("I want to pray to God").

The priest smiled and said, "Da. Toi muon cau-nguyen Chua cun vay" ("I also want to pray to God").

Torres knelt and the priest started his prayers, facing the altar.

When Torres and the priest had finished their prayers, Torres walked up to the priest and said, "I'll bring you some candles next time I come."

"Thank you, Co-Van."

Torres bowed in sign of respect, then he walked back to the Vietnamese compound.

Two days later, Gunny Tim came to pick Torres up and drive him back to where he could join the rest of the team at the OP.

"Torres, this is Lieutenant Gatlin. He's the new member of the team. We're also going to get a sergeant named Jensen. He'll be with us for a while. That way in case we have to split up the team, there will be three in each group. We're going to move south toward Quang Ngai province. We'll share the same AO with the Americal Division. We'll have some joint operations, and we may face the 48th Battalion," the captain said.

Torres noted that a beautiful puppy had been brought along and was to be considered the team mascot. "His name is Phuock," said Gunny.

"That's a very adequate name for him," said Lieutenant Mc-Duffie. "Just like a family; now we have a pet."

The young dog ran around the bunker and slept by someone's head at night. He never barked loudly and everyone seemed to enjoy his company.

Torres got orders to take Lieutenant Gatlin and pick up some more rations. They were to stay the night at the storage building and return the following day. Captain Johnson, Lieutenant McDuffie, Gunny Tim, and Sergeant Jensen were to remain at the OP.

When Lieutenant Gatlin and Torres returned to the OP, Torres noted that Phuock was nowhere in sight. He asked Gunny, "Hey, Tim, where is Phuock?"

"Torres, I didn't want to tell you, but yesterday he walked out into the minefield and was blown to bits."

"Gunny, that dog has never gone out of the bunker. Are you sure he *walked* out?"

"Yes, Torres. Sorry about that. I know you liked the dog. It's sad, but what can I say?"

"Well, I guess nothing. Poor Phuock. I see that the major's wife is still here."

"She came back yesterday, Torres."

"She looks like she's ready to cook something for the major."

"Corporal Tiep is going on leave, and we're going to collect some money so he can buy something for his two wives and the kids. They live in Da Nang, but in separate houses," said Gunny.

Torres said, "Tiep seems to be a nice fellow. I'll give him some money also. Who's collecting it, Gunny?"

"The lieutenant is, that is, Lieutenant McDuffie. Go and see him."

"Alright, Gunny," said Torres.

Torres went into the bunker and, handing some Vietnamese money to Lieutenant McDuffie, said, "Here, Lieutenant. This is for Corporal Tiep."

"Thank you, Sergeant. I see Gunny already told you."

"Umju."

"Well, right now, I am going to eat some khong cho," said the lieutenant.

He walked out the rear door. Torres looked at Jensen and said, "The lieutenant is going to eat dog again. These people never get tired of eating dog. When the lieutenant gets back, he can save a lot of money if he buys dog food because whoever eats dog can eat dog food also. Dog food is much cheaper than regular food. Give him some Purina Dog Chow."

"He may eat it," said Jensen.

"You know, Jensen, something is funny. The lieutenant said he was going to eat dog, and Phuock was blown up by a mine, according to Gunny. Something isn't right. Did you hear any mine explode?"

"No, I didn't."

"Are you sure?"

"I'm sure, Torres."

"Well, I think the lieutenant, the major, and his wife are gulping it down right now. I hope every time they open their mouths they bark. Poor Phuock. I'll miss him. He was a nice pet."

"I know," said Jensen.

Torres walked out to check over the area once more where Tim said Phuock had been blown up. He stood near the concertina and barbed wire and tried to spot the crater of an exploded mine. He could not see any unusual hole or fresh dirt spread around the area. There were no filled holes either that would indicate an explosion had occurred recently.

Torres doubted Tim's word about Phuock's fate, but he thought maybe Tim didn't want to hurt his feelings and that was why he was speaking with a forked tongue, as the Native Americans said when someone was not telling the truth. He said to himself, "I won't ask Tim any more about it. I'll just try to forget it."

15

Early the next day a meeting was called by Captain Johnson. "Alright, men, there is a mission we have to accomplish. It's a combination operation with some units of the Americal Division. We won't be on the same route of advance, but we may need some armor or artillery support from them. If need be, we'll call for it.

"The 48th Vietcong Battalion has been very active around the area south of Chulai and north of Quang Ngai. There is some indication that North Vietnamese regulation forces are moving to the high grounds of the area, following the Ho Chi Minh Trail. Also, there are some local guerrillas active around the area. We'll be operating around villages close to the city of Quang Ngai. There's a village named Song Tin and others. We'll get the word very soon about as to when we will be leaving."

Two days later the battalion got word to move by truck down Highway 1 south of Chulai and north of Quang Ngai. The truck stopped at the side of the highway and started to clear the areas all around.

The terrain was mostly covered by the usual plantations of rice paddies. There were also some sugar-cane fields; to the east, where the Yellow Sea was visible, were some coconut groves.

After advancing for almost three thousand yards while moving west, the unit reached an area where many guava trees were growing. They were spread out in bunches, and in places they were very tall and bulky. There were some hootches located a little father apart. The distances varied from three hundred to almost eight hundred yards.

The battalion commander ordered the unit to stop and set up defensive positions for the night. As there were six members in the advisory team and also an artillery forward observer from the Americal Division, who'd joined the team the day before the mission started, the radio watch for the night was going to be shorter for each of the team members.

About 1900 hours, as twilight approached, Torres walked around and stepped closer to a lone hootch that was nearby. His curiosity was aroused when he saw some security members coming from the opposite side of the house. Torres was standing to the rear, about fifty yards from the hootch. The staff had set up camp about two hundred yards from the hootch he was approaching. Suddenly he heard talk and some cries. The cries were those of a man.

Torres, trying not to let anyone become aware of his presence, sneaked in and saw a group of five soldiers, their weapons in their hands. One of them was the operations sergeant of the battalion. Torres looked at the ground and saw a man dressed in the customary pajamalike Vietnamese dress. He was digging a hole in the ground. He had already dug about three feet into the ground. He had a shovel in his hands and seemed to be very disturbed; he was crying. Two soldiers with their rifles at port arms were guarding him. The operations sergeant said to the four soldiers, two of whom were sitting by the hootch door with their weapons cradled in their arms, "When he finishes digging the hole, come and get me. I'm going to check with the major and see what he wants us to do with him."

Torres did not try to show himself to the sergeant or the men. He wanted to see what was going on. In his mind was the idea that maybe the man had been told to dig a hole as a defensive position for the night and the hole was to be used by some of the soldiers. It had happened before, or so he'd been told.

Torres walked back to the area where Gunny was and said, "Gunny, I just saw a man digging a foxhole. I wonder if he is a prisoner and they're going to evacuate him to the detention area in the morning?"

"It could be. It's quite late now, Torres. Maybe they'll wait until tomorrow."

"I hope so, Gunny."

Torres walked back to the same area he'd been in before; he noticed that the operations sergeant had returned and joined the four soldiers. He had apparently received orders as to what to do with the prisoner. Two soldiers were by the hole throwing the dirt back in. The man was standing inside the hole, very frightened and sobbing continuously; he was begging for mercy. The other two soldiers had their weapons aimed at the man's head. The sergeant was yelling at the man and asking questions. It was a very desperate situation for the poor man.

Torres walked over to the area and made his presence known. He looked at the sergeant; then the sergeant ordered the man to get out of the hole. The man had to crawl out of it and walk over to him. The soldiers had their weapons aimed at the man, and Torres moved closer toward the man as if to protect him from any unnecessary shooting. Without his asking, the operations sergeant said to Torres, "Co-Van, this man was in the major's unit before. He deserted years ago. The major said that he must be punished."

"Yes, Sergeant, but he should be court-martialed, not tortured."

"Yes, Co-Van. We will tie him and send him to jail tomorrow."

"Thank you, Sergeant. It will be good if you do that."

"Do not worry, Co-Van. Nothing is going to happen to him."

Torres walked back to where the rest of the staff was preparing for the night.

145

In the morning after securing his hammock and covering his dugout, Torres walked back to check if any of the people who had been with the prisoner or the prisoner himself was around. The operations sergeant was with the battalion commander, as was usual when the unit was in the midst of an operation. Torres walked to the front of the house and saw the foxhole the prisoner had dug. It was full except that the level of the dirt was slightly higher than before. He checked to see if there were any drops of blood around. He hoped that the man was safe and had been brought back to a secure place. He would ask the operations sergeant later on, and he would remark on it to the captain when they moved on.

The unit kept moving northwest until they reached a large plateau where some big buildings had been standing before. They were only tall walls left standing now. The structures apparently were two to three stories high. There was a wide dirt road running through the area, with indications that it had been paved a long time ago. In some areas there were patches of asphalt and gravel. The road led up to some high ground, with hills no higher than six hundred feet.

While the staff moved on up the road, Torres stayed slightly to the rear. There were some guava bushes, very tall in height, in patches along the way. Just as the group had almost cleared the destroyed buildings, Torres glanced at some guava bushes and saw some men partially concealed by the branches. They were talking.

Torres stopped and carefully peeped between the bushes. Once more he felt outraged at the sight that greeted him. Standing behind the bushes were four soldiers, members of the battalion, and to the front of them were two more figures. The four men were members of the reconnaissance platoon. One was a sergeant, who seemed to be in charge. But the presence of the two other human beings touched Torres's heart. They were two young boys. They seemed to be brothers, judging by their physical appearance; one was about twelve years old and the oldest about fourteen. Their hands were tied in front and they were sobbing, tears coursing down their cheeks. As Torres walked up, one of the soldiers untied the two young kids. The boys scrubbed their wrists, which were apparently numb. Torres could see the pressure marks of the ropes. Torres looked at the young boys; he was reminded of Victor Hugo's characters in his famous novel *Les Miserables*. The raggedy clothes of the kids were enough to make him sad; then as he looked up at the guava trees he realized that the kids had been strung up from the trees. He also saw a stick with no leaves and realized it had been used as a whip on the children's backs. The sergeant made the remark, "Maybe they don't know where the VC are. Let them go."

Torres immediately walked up and shielded the boys while he said, "Nhiu con di di. Di di mau" ("Boys, go, go. Go fast"). The young lads walked away uneasily and very shakily; they did not want to run as they were probably thinking that they could be shot. Torres made a remark and said to the sergeant, "Number ten, Trung Si." The sergeant walked away and did not even glance back.

The unit came up to a cliff where there was a river below that could be cross jumped over rocks and sandy banks. Torres looked over to the far side of the river and saw, about three hundred yards away, ten young females with bronzed skin and smooth, long black hair running down their shoulders. They ranged from eight to fourteen years old and they had a Polynesian appearance. Lieutenant Thiem came over and said to Torres, "Co-Van, those girls are Montagnards. The families live very close to here."

Torres looked over. Curiously the fact that they were all naked from the waist up was of no concern to him, but he saw some of them smiling and realized that their teeth had been sharpened, which he had been told was done in their culture.

They do it to young girls to prevent others from stealing them. It is like a self-preservation tradition in their way of life.

The staff came up to a huge crater, where many bunkers had been built. It was the Montagnards' camp, and a tall, dark-skinned man came up to meet the staff. The battalion commander and his staff were greeted very politely by the chief. Torres stayed at the end, and as everyone passed by, the chief shook hands with them.

Glancing at the chief's dress, Torres noticed that he wore an Eisenhower jacket with cut sleeves up to the ends of the upper arms. He noticed that the chief was very proudly wearing a couple of decorations. They were neither Vietnamese medals nor his own cultural and traditional ornaments; they were American decorations. Right below an American Infantry Combat Badge, which is awarded only to any American soldier who comes in contact with the enemy forces under combat conditions, the chief proudly displayed a Bronze Star.

The battalion operations sergeant, who understood the dialect spoken by the tribe, stood next to the chief as the staff walked by and greeted him. There were some members of the tribe standing next to and to the rear of the chief. Some of them had a couple of chickens in their hands. One of them had a bottle of some light white liquid, which resembled saki. As Torres approached, he immediately bowed his head in a show of respect to the chief. One of the men standing to the left of the chief took a sharp knife, cut off the head of the chicken he was holding, and poured the blood into a glass cup, which did not look to be very clean. The chief reached for a glass, which was immediately handed to him by another of his man. Pouring some of the liquid into the eight-ounce glass about halfway, he reached for the cup with the chicken blood in it and poured some into the already half-full glass. He stuck his index and middle finger into the glass, mixed the drink, touched Torres on his forehead and then touched himself, and in his unintelligible dialect said something to Torres. The operations sergeant said, as he translated the chief's message, "Co-Van, he said he wishes you a long life and that you kill many Vietcong."

"Sergeant, give him many thanks and a wish of long life to him also."

"Okay, Co-Van."

The sergeant gave the chief the message and Torres bowed once more to him. The chief handed Torres a bow and some arrows that he took from one of this men. Torres continued his walk and joined the staff, which was slowly moving ahead.

The battalion reached a ravine between two small hills about sixteen hundred yards from the Montagnard camp. The commander ordered the men to set up the customary perimeter defense for the night.

Torres asked Lieutenant Thiem, "Sir, I noticed that the chief of the Montagnard had some American decorations."

"Yes, Co-Van. He is a very brave man and they were given to him. Tonight when you hear drums and noises, do not worry. The Montagnards want to keep the bad spirits away."

"Sir, not only that. I think that they also want to show the Vietcong they are awake."

At 2200 hours, the drums and chanting from the Montagnards could be heard for miles around. "Aye, aye, aye." Boom, boom, boom, boom. It was steady, and the same rhythmical cadence continued into the morning hours.

The battalion continued to move and engaged in some sporadic contact with the enemy. The commander once more gave the order to move back and set defensive positions south of Song Tin and slightly to the north of the city of Quang Ngai. The area was well populated, with houses spread around. Some of the hootches were very large and in an L shape. There were many fruit trees around. Coconut palms, sour sop, and sugar cane were also growing. At a distance there were quite a few sugar-cane fields that had been recently burned out. Apparently it was done to prevent the Vietcong from hiding.

Torres noticed that there were Vietnamese pots similar to a wok and big cement ovens in which farmers apparently had boiled the cane juice to extract the sugar. It was the same method the Spanish and Puerto Ricans had used during the colonial era in the Antilles. They were primitive mills.

The staff was housed in a building which was owned by an elderly couple with a young daughter about twenty years old. She was a very beautiful lady, and from the time the staff occupied the house, she felt very uneasy. The three of them moved to one room while the staff, with the major, used two rooms. One room was a storage area for the owners of the house. The advisory team hung their hammocks from the trees next to the front patio and concealed in between.

Torres noticed how the girl felt and saw Lieutenant Thiem and a security sergeant talking to her while she went to the storage room to get some pots, apparently for cooking. The girl left the room she was sharing with her parents immediately, locking the front door of the room right after she entered.

Torres walked up to the lieutenant and said, "Lieutenant, why does the girl look so frightened? She looked like she didn't want to talk to you or any of the soldiers."

"Co-Van, it is not like that. I am going to tell you that this family has four more people. There are brothers and she is the only girl in the family. There are two boys who are younger than her and two who are older. But it is a bad thing what happened in her family."

"What, Lieutenant?"

"Co-Van, two boys are soldiers with the Vietnamese Army and the other two are Vietcong. It is like brothers against brothers."

"Lieutenant, you probably know about the Civil War in the United States. There are stories of families who hated each other. Castro in Cuba had a sister and they did not get along with each other's ideas. She had to get out of Cuba because Castro could put her in jail. But tell me, Lieutenant, do the parents know about it, and do they see their sons?"

"Yes, they come over sometimes and get together."

"Whoa! I hope it never gets to happen," said Torres.

"Happen? What, Co-Van?"

"Lieutenant, imagine if the brothers' units get involved in a skirmish in combat and they kill or hurt each other. I think their parents would die of sorrow."

"Yes, Co-Van, I hope it never happens."

"Me, too, Lieutenant. It would be very sad. Good night, Lieutenant."

"Good night, Co-Van."

When morning arrived, the battalion continued to check and clear the immediate area. There was dense vegetation and many trails from hamlet to hamlet. The sugar-cane fields were bigger and some were not burned or squashed down. The movement was getting slow, although once in a while the unit reached open areas planted with rice paddies. Contact with guerrilla forces of the 48th Battalion intensified. There were also some local guerrillas involved. Gunships from the American support units came on call to assist the battalion's advance, as well as some American units that were moving along the left flank of the battalion. They were sometimes in view of the staff and the advisory team. The American unit moving along to the immediate left was using armored personnel carriers with .50-caliber machine guns mounted on their turrets. They moved side by side with the battalion.

The Vietcong forces were on the run. The units drew close

to a wide river and the American units turned their heavy machine guns on the Vietcong, who could be seen swimming across.

The 4th Battalion continued its rapid forward movement and, using all the aircraft and artillery support from the American units, cleared areas quickly. There was not a chance for the men to stop, and the enemy was kept on the run continuously. The battalion had some casualties, but in comparison to the Vietcong the estimate was one to five. It had been the most sustained operation since Torres had arrived in the unit.

All along the entire operation, the units involved had been in contact with enemy forces, mainly the 48th Vietcong Battalion and some other local guerrillas.

16

The 4th Battalion was ordered to move and take positions to the north of Quang Ngai, near some villages that included My-Lai and the many hamlets around the area. Some enemy weapons and casualties were captured as the rifle companies cleared the immediate areas.

Torres said to Logan, "Look, I found some leaflets directed at American soldiers. It's unbelievable what they say. Look at this one."

Torres showed Logan a leaflet that said that on April 4, 1967, members of the 3rd Regiment, 4th Infantry Division, stationed at Dau-Tieng district, Thu-dau Mot province, refused to carry out mopping-up operations and fought against their commanders for thirty minutes; the result was fifty men wounded or killed, three helicopters destroyed, and thirteen big tents burned. "Look at this other one about Chulai. It says that one thousand men were killed and two hundred aircraft were destroyed."

"Torres, we know that's not true. We would be fools to believe it. Remember, we just came from Chulai and the base security is very good. I really don't know who they're trying to convince."

"Well, listen, I remember when I was in Kumwha Valley in Korea and the Chinese used to use the same type of propaganda. At Christmastime, they played records of Mario Lanza singing 'Ave Maria' and then announced over the speakers, 'American GI, last year MacArthur said, "Home by Christmas." He is back home, but you are still here. Remember, generals cannot fight wars without soldiers. Refuse to fight and come to us.' They used to keep us awake all night, which we didn't mind."

Gunny Tim came over and immediately said to Torres, "Hey, pal, the captain wants us to go to Tam-Ky to get some rations and water. If we leave now, we can be back early and have enough time to wash up and get clean clothes too. I heard you guys talking about propaganda. How about the values of our heads? Did you know that the Vietcong have offered a ransom for our heads?"

"Well, Gunny, I heard you talking about it the other day while we were at the OP."

"For a captain, they'll pay $10,000. For a lieutenant $8,000 and for a guy like me, maybe $6,000 to $7,000."

"For me, I don't care if they give one penny, because the less you're worth, the less they try to get you. It's fine with me. Let them look for the expensive ones, Gunny."

"You know, Torres, you're right. Now let's go and do what the captain said."

"Alright, Gunny. I'm ready to go."

The two men walked over to the jeep, which had been brought up by the security personnel as usual. Sergeant Fong drove it and was accompanied by Hoi.

The two men departed for Tam-Ky. They would stop at Chulai and also see Sergeant Stephens, the mess sergeant.

"You saw the old jeep parked at Stephens's mess. I talked to the captain. The major wants to get it fixed up. It will be another vehicle we can use, or the staff can also ride in it when needed. The major had a couple of AK 47s and I can give them to Steve. I'll stop on our way to Tam-Ky and tell him we'll get the jeep on our way back. The major can get us a mechanic, or it can be hauled back by another vehicle."

Two days later the battalion received orders to move back to the Tam-Ky area and assume a defensive posture. The rifle companies were dispersed from the north to the northwest and would serve as security for District Headquarters and political prisoners of war prison, the other adjacent operations center. The Vietnamese military compound was also under their protection.

During the day, since not too much enemy activity was expected, the advisory team had enough time to tend to many personal things. This included going to Chulai and the MACV compound and even visiting a restaurant with the battalion commander, who'd invited the team for lunch. The restaurant was located along Highway 1 in the center of Tam-Ky. Shrimp was served as the main course.

Christmas was only a couple of days away and the advisory team was invited to attend a Christmas program prepared by the personnel at the MACV compound. The program was to be presented on Christmas Eve. Some of the boys dressed as girls and it was very entertaining. They sang Christmas carols, danced, and recited. Everyone felt very enthusiastic. The advisory team returned back to Tam-Ky immediately after the program was over.

The battalion staff and the advisory team occupied some zinc buildings that were located next to District Headquarters. There were Army cots to sleep on. The buildings were reinforced around with sandbags, which would protect the occupants from any ground fire. It was very safe.

On Christmas night everything was normal and almost quiet, except for the usual firing of flares and some artillery rounds fired at suspected enemy positions.

Christmas Day came and even the battalion commander had the spirit. He invited the advisory team for a special lunch. Christmas carols were also sung. Torres did his share by singing a favorite of his. He remembered a favorite singer of his named Felipe Rodriguez, who interpreted ballads and tangos. Torres didn't care whether he could sing or not; he sang a ballad about the three Wise Men. It was a brief party but everyone enjoyed it.

The battalion continued all along in its defensive role except for patrolling the area and setting up ambushes in case the enemy tried to surprise them. There were rumors that some guerrillas were going to come into the city and launch an attack from within it.

Days passed and New Year's Eve came; everyone welcomed in 1968. There were thirty-one more days before Vietnam would celebrate their New Year or Tet; it would fall on the 31st of January.

Corporal Tiep once in a while invited Torres to eat some of the food he'd prepared and sometimes Tim or Torres gave him money and some beef or pork, which they would get from their friends at the compound outside Chulai. The corporal also cooked some fish, which he could buy at the market.

"Hey, Tiep, what is this meat you made? It tastes good," said Torres.

"Co-Van, it is number one. I am glad you like it."

"But what is it, Hasi?"

"Co-Van, that is chicken tripe mixed with fish tripe."

"Well, Tim, you've been eating it for a long time and you haven't lost any weight. If it's good for you, it should be good for me. When I go back home I'll tell my wife, Elsa, to make soup out of it and not to throw away any chicken guts or fish guts either."

"Yeah, Torres, she may run you out of the house, or she may tell *you* to eat it all. I doubt your wife will cook it for you."

"I know. I was just kidding. She likes chicken liver and the gizzards, but I don't know of anyone eating chicken tripe at home. But, Gunny, you should eat dog. The American Indians used to eat dog. I read that in a history book."

"Torres, my great-great-grandaddy probably did it, but that does not mean that this great-great-grandson is going to do it if it's not necessary."

Mid-January came and the battalion was airlifted to high ground between Quang Tri province and Quang Nam province.

156

Wide rivers and dense vegetation characterized the area. Many banana plants could be spotted on the hills and all over the areas facing west and north; some coal mines were also visible. There were some Marine units also involved in the operation. Some generals from the Marine brigades flew in in choppers and met the battalion staff and the advisory team. The operation lasted for a week.

The battalion was split up, and some units were airlifted north of the old capital of Hue. It was the old imperial capital, almost surrounded by the Perfume River. Lieutenant Thiem called Torres and said, "Co-Van, this area is very important to all Vietnamese people. It is very special."

"Why, Lieutenant? I see beautiful pagodas and a very beautiful Catholic church. You have that in other cities in Vietnam, don't you?"

"Yes, Co-Van, but you see the citadel over there?"

"Yes, I do," Torres answered.

"Well, Co-Van, the Vietnam queen still lives in there. The people respect her. She has servants and she is well-protected."

"I didn't know that, Lieutenant. Thank you for the information. If I can go shopping in Hue, I'd like to see more. Maybe you and whoever else wants to go can accompany me. We shouldn't be here for too long and probably we'll move back before Tet."

"Yes, I know. In one week we will be back. Maybe before," said Lieutenant Thiem.

"I was told that the reason why we came here is because the North Vietnamese may start to move troops down south and use the seashores. Is that right, Lieutenant? The 10th Division is supposed to defend this area, but they are now moving north and northwest with all the regiments. They're all over the Ho Chi Minh Trail and west of this road."

"Yeah, Co-Van. That's the truth. Do you know what the people call this road?"

"Don't tell me, Lieutenant. This is the famous Street without Joy."

"That's right, Co-Van."

"Well, I read a lot about your history. I don't know all, but I know some."

"Co-Van, that is why you understand many things about the people here. It is good."

Five days later and with only five days left before the 31st of January, the battalion moved back to the same area they had once occupied to the north and northwest of Tam-Ky and next to District Headquarters and the prisons.

Torres brought some candles and visited the old priest he had shared a prayer with. Hoi accompanied him. He also gave the priest some canned peaches like the ones Stephens had given him weeks before. The man was very honored by Torres's visit and together they prayed once more in front of the improvised altar.

17

The staff moved into the inner yard of the political prison. The advisory team also dug foxholes for their protection in the yard and close to the corridors, which were covered with awnings along the center and the north and south wings. The political jail was built in a squared U-shape with only one floor and resembling an American motel. The roof was covered with curved red clay tiles leaning at a 45-degree angle.

There were ten cells in each of the opposite wings and fifteen in the center. A corridor six feet wide extended from in-between the north wing and the north side of the center row of cells. There was also a hallway, which led up to the bunkers and defensive positions located to the north; the hallway was located between the seventh and eighth cells from west to east. The first three rooms to the north of the center row of cells were used as offices and interrogation rooms. Each of them had a wooden desk facing north with a single chair behind it. There were two extra chairs; one faced the desk and the chair of the interrogator. The other chair was near the east wall and not more than two feet away. Every room was alike. There was another room in each of the interrogation rooms; these were located to the east. These were also cells, as the only door leading to them indicated. The doors were located about six feet from the right-hand corner of the interrogator's desk. The walls were of solid cement, ten to twelve inches thick. Each room was ten feet from the floor to the inner part of the ceiling.

The prisoners' cells each had a small cutaway window located at the center bottom of the steel door. The windows were six inches in the vertical angle and one foot horizontally.

The prisoners received water, and as Torres saw, only one meal was served daily. It consisted mostly of boiled rice and some sort of vegetable. The meal was served on a tin plate. A pair of chopsticks was placed flat across the center of the plate over the food. The water was served in a tin cup.

Torres wondered about the prisoners' personal hygiene, including their physiological needs. He glanced at an empty, half-opened cell and saw a white plastic bucket. More than likely that was used as a toilet. The Vietnamese used a piece of log for a pillow, rounded around the middle and placed behind and under the back of the neck. And there was one log inside each cell. There were no linens. The front door of each cell had a sliding, rounded bar clamped down and secured with a heavy bronzed padlock. Also, there was a side hinge above each bar and another heavy padlock. Every door was made of solid iron three feet wide and six feet tall. There were no windows that could be opened or shut, and the only air and light that could penetrate the rooms came from a small, squared opening centered on the back wall of each cell. Vertically they were about twelve inches long and horizontally not more than four inches in width. There were no bars.

To Torres, the cells resembled the described cells of Devil's Island, where the famous Papillon was interned. Apparently they had been built by the French during their occupation of Indochina.

Torres dug his foxhole two feet from the extreme corner to the right of the south wing, where it met the center row of cells. The rest of the team had their foxholes dispersed at intervals. Gunny Tim was about thirty feet away from Torres, and he was the closest. Two security soldiers and Sergeant Fong's foxholes were dug next to Torres's along the south wing and at a distance of twenty feet between each position.

It was the 27th of January and only four days before Tet, the Chinese New Year, when four prisoners were brought in for interrogation and apparently to be confined. They were blindfolded, with black bandanas tied at the backs of their heads. Two of the prisoners were women in their midthirties; the other two were men about the same age as the women. They were dressed in the customary black pajamas that many Vietnamese wore. The two most popular colors are white and black.

Besides the blindfold, the prisoners had their arms locked around a pole crossed behind their backs, and their forearms were tied in front at their wrists. They were barefoot and wet. The women had their heads lowered, and all four prisoners were very silent.

The two men were turned over to the two guards, who proceeded to remove the locking wooden bar from each and took off their blindfolds. They immediately took the men and moved them to two separate cells along the inner hallway between the north wing and the center line of cells. They locked up the men, then both guards returned to receive the two women. A man who seemed to be in charge of the jail and had the duty of interrogator also proceeded to order the two guards to move the two women into the third room from the north end. They removed the locking bars and the blindfolds from both of the women, who appeared to be very tense and submissive.

Torres watched discreetly, seemingly unaware of what was happening. Apparently he was the only curious one because, glancing around, he noticed that the other members of the team were looking at a map of the area and plotting coordinates for artillery support in case of need.

Torres noticed that he could not see the inside of the cell where the two women had been directed to enter by command of the guards so he walked slowly to the center of the patio, where he could continue to indirectly observe the actions of the jailers and the reactions of the subjugated women. He saw that one

161

woman had been separated from the others and placed inside one of the inner cells, which was located opposite the front door. Just like the other outside cells, it also had a steel door with a hinge and a padlock attached.

The other woman was pulled by one of the guards and made to stand facing south toward a wooden desk, which was about four feet from the wall. There was a chair behind it and the man giving orders sat in it. One of the guards took a bent stick about a half inch in width, which had apparently been cut from a guava bush. He started to twist and bend it as though intimidating the sobbing woman. The guard struck the air with the stick like a cowhand lashing at cattle to make them move.

The interrogator started to ask questions and the woman nodded her head up and down as a sign of affirmation and surrender. Suddenly one of the guards realized that Torres could see what they were doing, although he did not suspect that Torres had watched what had happened up to that instant. He moved up to the front door and half-closed it just as the woman kneeled in front of the desk. Torres could not see what was happening.

Three minutes later the door opened and both women were taken out of the room and placed inside two separate cells in two empty rooms of the north wing of the jail. The woman who had been interrogated had her shirt partially pulled down her back and some bruises were visible, as though she had been lashed.

Torres walked up to Lieutenant Thiem and asked in Vietnamese, "Lieutenant, tai sao?" ("Why?")

The Lieutenant answered, "What are you talking about, Co-Van?"

"Lieutenant, I just saw two women, who were brought in as prisoners, being mistreated. The Geneva Convention prohibits that. All prisoners should be treated fairly and respected. How do we expect to win their minds and hearts if the same people mistreat each other?"

"Co-Van, the guards and people who work here do what they are told to do."

"But it is wrong, Lieutenant. They are considered enemies, yes, but they are human beings first. I don't think there is any need for mistreatment. You know, Lieutenant, back in America there are many instances of prejudice and mistreatment between races and right here I see it between your own."

"Co-Van, if you had to defend yourself, would you kill somebody?"

"Sure, I'd try to do it. In fact, Lieutenant, you may hear that people consider themselves patriots up to the end, saying, 'I'd give my life for my country.' When people go to war that is exactly their battle cry, just as the Japanese say, 'Banzai.'"

"What do you mean, Co-Van?"

"What I mean, sir, is that the person who says, as sometimes you may, 'If I go to war, I am going to make the other fellow give his life for his country because if I am dead, I will not be able later on to enjoy the things I fought for.' Some day this war will be over and monuments will be built and streets and towns will be renamed for heroes. Dead heroes."

"You are right, Co-Van; but remember, if a Vietcong comes toward you, fire first and ask questions later, unless he is trying to surrender and has laid his weapon down."

"Well, Lieutenant, any person who surrenders should be treated fairly."

"In here the people mistreat each other, as you see. Sometimes they feel frustrated and that is why they act the way they do, Co-Van."

"Sir, I have to go and get some clean clothes. I'm going to ask Captain Johnson to let me walk back to the storage room and get it. I'll ask Hoi to take some dirty clothes to the laundry for me. I'll see you, sir."

"Chao, Co-Van."

163

Torres walked up to where the captain was and said to him, "Captain, I have to get some clean clothes and also have Hoi take some to the laundry. I can walk back to the storage room and do it if you'll permit it."

"Yes, Sergeant Torres, you can go; also, get some rations if you need some."

"Thank you, sir. I'll see you later. I won't be long."

Torres departed, shouldering his M2 automatic carbine beside his pistol, strapped to his left shoulder with the hand grip facing backward. He could easily reach for it with his right hand and quickly draw it if needed. He had changed his M14 for a carbine M2 two weeks before, at the MACV compound.

Just before leaving, Torres walked through the hallway that was located in between the seventh and eighth cells of the north wing of the jail. He wanted to familiarize himself with the area. He stopped in view of a row of bunkers and defensive positions connected by a long trench that was only about three feet in depth. In front of the long trench was a double apron fence running from east to west; also, as an extra obstacle for any attacking forces approaching from the north, there was a concertina wire paralleling the double apron fence.

Attached to the wire were tin cans with small stones inside. The cans were hanging loosely, suspended by small pieces of wire hooks. Anyone coming in contact with the fences would make the cans rattle and warn the defenders.

18

Torres walked back into the patio and headed for the front gate. He opened the right side of the steel gate and, after stepping out, closed it. There were two sentinel positions reinforced by sandbags at each side of the entrance, and there were two guards in each. They were military police, as their left arm bands indicated with the words QUAN CANH.

Torres walked down the road in a southerly direction and came up to the District Headquarters Building. After he passed by, he turned left and reached the front of the building of the Counterintelligence Operations Center, where he saw one of the young Puerto Ricans who had been released by the Vietcong over a month before. He thought they should have been back with their families by then. He'd heard rumors about some papers being found by friendly forces in which the young men accused the U.S. government of intervening in Vietnam's affairs. He thought that if it were true about the documents, they'd probably written them under stress and been forced to sign them. There were also rumors about an American black man leading some Vietcong forces around the Quang Tri and Quang Nam provinces.

Torres continued to walk toward the Vietnamese compound. In five minutes he reached the open front gate. He headed for the storage building and, at the same time, looked around to see if he could see Hoi. Maybe Hoi was talking to someone as he normally did or was visiting a family he knew.

Torres reached the building and opened the storage room. He walked in, and unlocking the padlock of his duffel bag, he pulled out some clean underwear and a couple of handkerchiefs. He also took out some shoe polish and spread some on his jungle boots. He was checking two uniforms that were on wire hangers and connected by a nail in the wall when he heard voices outside. He recognized Hoi's voice talking to someone. He walked out the door and saw that Hoi's companion was Sergeant Fong. Torres said, "Chao, Trung Shi Fong, Chao Hoi."

Both men said, almost in unison, "Chao, Co-Van."

"Hoi, I need you to do me a favor. Can you take my dirty clothes to the laundry?"

"Yes, I'll do it right now. It will only take me ten minutes."

"Okay, I'll wait for you and we can walk back together, unless you're staying here."

"No, I'm not staying here. I will go back with you; also Trung Shi Fong is going back. We can all walk back together."

"Okay, I'll wait for you. Meanwhile, I'll write a letter to my wife and daughters."

Hoi departed with the dirty clothes, which were wrapped in a bundle. Sergeant Fong walked over to a hootch that was located directly in front of the storage building and started a conversation with a mamasan.

Torres walked back inside the room and picked up some stationery. He started to write, "Dear Mayi and girls. I am okay and I hope you are fine. The Vietnamese New Year, which is called Tet, is only a couple of days away. By the time you receive this, it will probably be over. It seems that the time is flying by. The sooner my rotation date comes, the better. I think I will be going out to the field for at least one more month, then after that I will probably be assigned to a desk job in some compound. They try to keep the advisors in the field for only six months, and unless the person volunteers, he may have a desk job until his tour of duty is over. It does not mean that it is always safe in a compound, but there are many facilities. I can eat a hot meal every day and also have pressed uniforms."

The letter continued, "The battalion is now protecting the prisoners' jails in this area of Tam-Ky, which was the first place I came to when I joined the rest of the team. Sometimes I see very bad things, and I wish I could do something about them. I do try many times. The people in here are very passive but also cruel with their own. I have read about it before in history books, and it seems that it is part of their tradition and culture in general. Do not worry about me; I can take care of myself. The rest of the team is also okay.

"The two boys released by the Vietcong should be back in Puerto Rico or wherever they live. I already wrote you that they were Puerto Ricans and had been released last month. I heard they found some papers in which they apparently accuse the United States of getting involved in this war. They probably wrote the letters under duress. It could be just propaganda.

"Well, this is all for now. I will write to you again soon. The best to the dogs, and I am glad they were not born here. Best to all the rest of the family and to you three, many kisses and hugs. Love you, your dear husband, Porfi."

Hoi returned from town and the talk outside alerted Torres to his presence. Torres secured his clothes and walked outside. He locked the door of the storage room and said to Hoi, "Let's go. I've got everything I need. Thank you, Hoi, for taking my laundry."

"Is okay, Co-Van. You are welcome."

The three men started to walk back to the jail.

"You wrote a letter home, Co-Van?"

"Yes, I did, Hoi. I told my wife I'm okay and that Tet will be coming soon. My daughters may not know that you celebrate the New Year on a different day than we do. This year is the Year of the Monkey or what, Hoi?"

"Co-Van, it is the Year of the Monkey."

When the three men reached the end of the straight road that led up to Provincial Headquarters and had turned right, they saw a young man riding a bicycle ahead of them. On the back of the vehicle he had a square box with a tin cover. The young man was stopped by two soldiers who were standing by the side of the road. The two soldiers pulled out some Vietnamese money and gave it to the young man, who in turn opened the lid of the tin box and pulled out two Cokes. He gave the two cans to the soldiers, who opened them and started to drink.

Torres asked Hoi and Sergeant Fong, "Do you want to drink a Coke? I'll pay for them."

"Okay, Co-Van, we will drink one."

"Please, Hoi. Tell the young man that we want three Cokes."

"Yes, Co-Van."

Hoi immediately relayed the message and the young man, who was about sixteen years old, opened the box again and gave each man a can. Torres, showing the young man and Hoi that he could help himself with the little Vietnamese he knew, asked the young man, "Bao Nhieu tien?" ("How much money?")

The young man smiled and answered, "Ba mot tram dong, Bac Mi."

Torres paid him the three hundred piaster he asked for and said, "Cam on Ong."

The young man took the three bills of one hundred each, and as he mounted his bike he said, "Tieng chao, trong ngay" ("Good-bye and a good day").

The three men continued their walk back and entered the patio of the jail, where Hoi opened the gate.

19

The next day was as quiet as the first and on the 30th of January the battalion commander ordered his staff to move and set up positions outside the jail's patio. None of them were offered any overhead protection. There were four zinc buildings located to the north, two hundred meters to the front and outside of the concertina and double apron fences. The distance from the jail walls to the buildings was four hundred meters.

The major moved with the staff and the advisory team to the first building in line from east to west facing north. To the north and east of the buildings the area was wide open and a huge rice plantation extended up to Route 1. Vehicles could be seen moving up north and south at a distance of 1,200 yards to the right.

The rice field, broken into paddies, made visual observation of any troop movement quite impossible, due to the dirt banks of the rice paddies separating each from the other. Any guerrilla force in sizeable quantity could get close to the staging area before it would be noticed; once there they could easily overrun the positions.

Torres thought that the situation was very critical and he asked the operations officer, "Sir, do you have any security dispersed out in the rice paddies?"

"Yes, we do. We also have ambushes. If the VC come, we'll know. There will also be patrols walking out the perimeter."

"I hope so. I don't like this area."

"Don't worry, Co-Van. We will be ready."

"That's easy for you to say." Torres looked over to Gunny Tim, who had hung his hammock already from a center beam to a wall beam about the middle of the building; walking over to the first beam from the rear entrance, he pulled his hammock from the back of his backpack and started to tie one of the rope ends.

"Gunny, you heard what I said to the operations officer."

Torres had dug his one-man foxhole facing the rice field and southwest from the staging area. The position was located about sixty yards from the building's door, facing south. He could move from his hanging hammock to his foxhole in ten seconds. Facing the rice paddies to his front, he constructed a parapet where he could lean his left forearm under his weapon and deliver effective fire upon any enemy force moving in a 90-degree angle from right to left. The parapet also gave him protection from the left and right flanks' ground fire. The hole was four feet in depth and wide enough to maneuver around. Behind the parapet and to the right, he'd dug a hole where he could accommodate some extra ammunition, including hand grenades. He had with him ten magazines full of ammunition for his carbine. Each magazine could hold thirty rounds. The magazines were tied in pairs facing opposite ends, where it was easy to switch an empty magazine around when the ammunition had been completely fired from one end.

Torres's experiences in Korea and the recent operations he had been in had come to be valuable. His weapons were very clean and oiled. His bayonet was sharp and clean. He carried his gas mask and checked it for proper functioning. The automatic firing selector of his carbine was in the automatic position. He had six hand-fragmentation grenades, as well as one smoke, one white phosphorus, and two tear-gas grenades. His steel helmet was properly camouflaged and his flak jacket on at all times. Torres was really ready for the action he anticipated, although nobody had told him about any imminent attack by the enemy on a night like Tet.

170

Torres noted that the general mood of the troops in the battalion was somber and uneasy. Like him it seemed that everyone anticipated some kind of action at any time. There was only one day before Tet. The question was, "Will the Vietcong spoil the New Year celebration?" It was just a matter of waiting and being ready for it.

At 1800 hours, Torres walked over to where Corporal Tiep was doing his cooking for the major and his staff. "Ha-Si Tiep, will you give me a small bowl of rice. I want to mix it with some beans from my C rations."

"Sure, Co-Van. Any time you need rice, just come in and ask. I will give it to you. Just ask for it, and if I do not have any, I will get it for you," said Tiep.

"Thanks, Ha-Si. I really appreciate it," Torres said as Ha-Si Tiep handed him a full bowl of rice and at the same time said, "You are welcome, Co-Van."

Torres returned back to his building; taking a heating tablet from his pack and a can of pork and beans, he proceeded to warm his meal. He mixed the rice into the dish. While he was eating his meal, he glanced at some of the staff members; he continued to sense their uneasiness and preoccupation. He saw a corporal pointing at him while he was talking to the others. Gunny Tim walked in and Torres said, "Tim, I don't like the way things look; too much secrecy."

Lieutenant McDuffie walked in as Torres was making his remark and asked, "Why did you say that, Sergeant Torres?"

"Well, I don't know, but my feeling is that something is about to happen tonight. We'd better stay alert and keep both eyes open."

Nobody made any more remarks.

The captain came in just before 1900 hours and immediately set the radio watch for the night. "Torres, you take the radio watch. There will be three hours for each of us. We'll start at 2000 hours. The lieutenant will take the second and Gunny the third. I'll take the last. If you want to change your watch between yourselves, you can do it; just be sure you tell the rest of the team so the right man will be called."

"Well, I doubt anyone would like to go to sleep tonight. I'll try to keep myself awake all night," said Torres.

As hours went by, radio silence was kept after 2200 hours, as directed by higher headquarters. Hour after hour went by and the only sound to be heard was the bang of an occasional flare fired by the artillery units located at far distances from the battalion's position. Flares could be seen all over the perimeter of the city of Tam-Ky and the adjacent villages. Almost every twenty to thirty minutes a flare illuminated the area to the front of the location of the staff.

Twenty-four hundred hours arrived and with it the Chinese New Year; 0100 hours, 0200, 0300, up to 0500 hours passed, and the same conditions prevailed.

At 0525 hours, automatic and small-arms fire was heard coming from the southwest direction, in respect to the staff's location. Estimating the distance, the action was approximately between 1,600 and 1,800 yards away. The radio silence was broken, and reports came in that the enemy had tried to infiltrate and broken through the lines to the west of the prisoners of war compound.

The fighting intensified as the firing of the weapons and the detonations of grenades, artillery, and mortars were heard. Everyone was on the alert around the battalion perimeter when suddenly small-arms fire was heard and some bullets hit the zinc buildings. Torres, very alert, looked around and didn't see anybody standing by. It seemed that everyone had scattered and moved into their foxholes. Torres ran out of the building and immediately jumped into his foxhole and a burst of flying bullets from an AK47 zoomed over his head. Mortar fire began to hit positions to the right rear of Torres's location. At the same time the firing of weapons intensified around Torres and all over the city of Tam-Ky. The enemy forces had launched an all-out attack on Quang Tin province and all over South Vietnam.

Torres kept on alert and constantly watched his frontal field of fire. He could make out some human-size figures moving at a far distance and advancing in his direction, although the morning light had not arrived in full yet. Men were moving closer, but the embankments of the rice paddies concealed the size of the advancing force as well as their direction, making it very hard to pinpoint and deliver effective fire on them.

The enemy continued to get closer and closer; the leading elements were already five hundred yards away from Torres's position. Torres noticed that the lights of the artillery flares and the high-explosive artillery shells falling all over and around the area made it easier for him to fire at the moving figures and slow them up.

Torres noticed that he was the only one firing his weapon and thought for a moment that his buddies and members of the battalion on line were waiting until the enemy could get closer and on a prearranged signal surprise the enemy and cut them down to bits. That was okay with him. He could inflict some casualties on the enemy as he could see many of them moving. He was probably the only one who could see them. He thought he would wait and see and keep doing what he was doing.

The enemy had already moved within four hundred yards and Torres thought that the forces to his left and right would definitely start firing their weapons. It had to be; the enemy was close enough already.

Torres continued for moments to think that he was the only one spotting targets to the front. The fire bursts from his automatic carbine were doing a good job, and he was accurate. He saw bodies falling down and getting up. But there were more of the enemy; and they continued determinedly to move forward by leaps and bounds. Torres did not want to run out of ammunition;

he had to make every shot count. One, two, three, four bodies cut down by his automatic fire.

As the enemy closed in to within three hundred yards, Torres still did not hear even one shot from his right or left against the advancing force. Was he alone? Was everyone hurt, wounded, or dead? It was better not to think about it. It could not be! They had to be there! Torres could not understand why they were not helping him. Had they moved back without warning him? Why did they not say something? He took quick glances to the right and left and saw no one, as a burst of rounds from an AK47 zoomed over his head.

Mortar fire began hitting positions to Torres's right and left. Maybe the enemy was using what they called "the bracketing method," pinpointing his position, and one of the next barrages would come over and hit his foxhole. The small-arms fire continued from his front, hitting and striking the ground all around him.

Torres still paid attention to the front and fired his weapon. He realized that the enemy was closer; at least within 250 yards. Up to now he had succeeded in keeping back the fast and steady advance of the aggressive forces. Still, he was the only one firing his weapon at the enemy, and he might not be able to hold out much longer. He needed some help. Once more Torres wondered if his buddies were close by to give him a hand. He could not be alone. They could not have moved out and left him to manage a sizable force by himself like the one moving toward him. Why weren't they firing?

Torres continued to deliver fire, and for a few seconds it seemed that the enemy halted in their assault. Maybe his friends and the others could see Torres and they would come back and give him the assistance he badly needed. But even as slowly as the enemy was moving forward, they continued to get closer and closer by the minute.

Torres only had two magazines of ammunition left out of

thirty rounds each. They were taped together. He had not heard screams or sounds from friendly troops as he glanced once more to his right and left. He had to pay attention to his field of fire. He hoped that the leading elements were no closer than the two hundred yards he had already calculated.

Torres pulled out a fragmentation hand grenade. Perhaps some of the enemy soldiers had closed in by crawling and were nearing his position. He pulled the safety pin of the grenade and, releasing its safety latch, counted mentally, "One thousand one, one thousand two, one thousand three, one thousand four." He threw the grenade as far as he could and the small hand bomb traveled through the air and exploded about ten feet off the ground, reaching the closer embankments of the rice paddies.

He had succeeded in his first try, and Torres decided to do it three more times. The grenades exploded in the air, spreading their deadly fragments over the frontal area from right to left. The training Torres had learned in his younger years and which he had later passed on to many was working; it had turned out to be useful when most needed. Now he only had two fragmentation grenades left. If the situation became more critical, he could use them. Meanwhile, the bullets continued to zoom over his head and strike the immediate area.

Torres realized that he only had two full magazines for his carbine and probably it was not enough to face a determined and sizable force like the one to his front. He thought the odds were against him. He had only one choice. His only chance of survival, if it was going to happen, was to move back by leaps and bounds and zigzag from position to position. He was not going to give the enemy forces the chance to take a straight shot at him.

The enemy for sure was already two hundred yards away, and Torres's chances would magnify if he used his only hand smoke grenade to conceal his retrograde movements. He pulled the grenade's safety pin and threw it about fifty yards to his left front. The wind, carrying the smoke curtain, dispersed from left to right and covered all the immediate area to Torres's front. It worked!

Torres climbed out of his foxhole, and facing the enemy's advancing direction, in a quick motion he fired his weapon, sweeping from left to right, hoping to curtail any enemy movement behind the smoke screen. He turned around and zigzagged about fifty meters and assumed the prone position behind a small dirt embankment. He could not see anyone but he knew they were out there. He rapidly did the same three more times, until he reached the area behind the third metal building. There he saw a body lying on its back. Torres looked over and recognized the wounded man; it was Lieutenant Tuck, the second rifle company commander.

Not hesitating, Torres kneeled. Realizing that the lieutenant had a severe stomach wound, he pulled out one of his cigarettes, lit it, and quickly placed it in the lieutenant's mouth. The lieutenant looked over, making a gesture of thanks, knowing now that he was not alone. Torres did not want the young officer to go into shock. Looking over, he saw a blanket that one of the security soldiers had left next to a foxhole. It was to his left and only a few feet away. He went over and took the blanket and started to place it over the lieutenant. Torres noticed that he was not the only one with the wounded man. A young Vietnamese soldier came over to help him.

Torres realized that the wounded lieutenant was clearly exposed to ground fire. He decided to move him behind a dirt bank that was five feet away. The young soldier helped him. Dragging the officer with care but as fast as possible, the two moved the lieutenant, who closed his eyes, still holding the cigarette in his left hand. The lieutenant said, "Cam on, Co-Van" ("Thank you, Advisor").

Torres looked around to check if there were any more friendly troops around. He saw Lieutenant McDuffie with a corporal and a young soldier, members of the security platoon.

They were inside a foxhole about fifteen yards away. The foxhole was wide enough to give them protection and also allow them to fire their weapons if needed. Torres walked over quickly; the young soldier ran up to the concertina wire and followed the path to the trenches behind the apron fence.

Torres looked over the left rear where the lieutenant and two men were and saw a sergeant, who was the squad leader of a rifle platoon. He was lying on his side with a wound on his left calf. Torres stood up and as he neared the lieutenant's position, a sudden burst of rounds from an AK47 zoomed in front of his face, almost blinding him. It hit the nearest corner of the third building. Torres immediately realized that the enemy was already inside the walls of the citadel. The shooting was coming from a standing tower located to the east of the political jail. The enemy had reached the buildings around the jail and were attacking the District Headquarters Building.

The lieutenant yelled to Torres, "Get down." Torres assumed the prone position, and looking over to where the sergeant was lying down, he crawled over and pulled out his first-aid kit. He opened the bandage package and wrapped it around the sergeant's thigh, applying pressure to hold down the pain and the blood. The young sergeant, very gratefully and with a smile on his face, said, "Co-Van, number one, Co-Van number one."

"Thank you," Torres replied. Torres then helped the sergeant take cover behind a mound of dirt, near a foxhole that contained a dead soldier.

Torres looked over to check for the lieutenant and the others and again found that he was alone, except for the two wounded men he had just helped. He looked over to his abandoned position and knew that the enemy had reached it. They were all over the first building area, regrouping to continue the assault. Torres pulled out one of his hand grenades and threw it as far as he could. Once more he did the same to obtain an air burst. There was only one clip of ammunition for his carbine. He changed the empty magazine by turning it around and locked the full magazine in place. He fired his weapon toward the first building, hoping to inflict some damage on the enemy scattered throughout the area. He ran out of ammunition for his carbine, but he still had his pistol, with four full magazines and eight rounds in each.

Torres slung his carbine, with the attached bayonet, over his left shoulder and pulled his pistol out of his shoulder holster. He took a quick look to his front and, turning around, zigzagged in his withdrawal until he had reached the concertina wires; then he followed the path back toward the command bunker. He kept his pistol ready and pointed toward the sky.

20

When Torres neared the bunker door, he saw three soldiers standing by, their weapons cradled in their arms. He holstered his pistol and walked up to the door of the bunker. He walked in about two feet from the exit and heaved a sigh of relief when he saw the battalion commander and Captain Johnson sitting there. Lieutenant McDuffie was sitting to the right of the captain. To the extreme right was the operations sergeant. Everyone was alive.

Gunny Tim came in, took a quick glance, and walked out toward the prison yard. He said to Torres, "Hi, Torres. Everything alright?" Torres did not answer and Gunny immediately departed as if he was in a hurry.

Torres looked to the officer and spoke to the major, who was in a daze, feeling that everything was lost. The major had his head down and was holding his forehead with his hands, his elbows resting on his thighs. He rocked back and forth as a child would who was falling asleep and hoped that he could close his eyes. The captain sat by looking at him, apparently waiting for a word.

Torres, without hesitation, said, "Sir, give me some men and I'll go out there and push them out. Give me a squad."

The major did not answer. Once more Torres looked over at the operations sergeant and said, "Give me some men. I'll go out there and push them out. I need some ammunition. Give me some men."

Nobody said a word. Torres shook his head. He thought if he were going to die, he would stand a chance of surviving if he fought back. He looked over to the left of the operations sergeant and saw some magazines he could use for his carbine. There were only four and they were not tied together, but it did not make any difference. He reached for five hand grenades and walked out of the bunker, still shaking his head. He could not understand why he had not gotten the help he needed or at least an answer. He thought he deserved that much at least; he was not going to stand idle.

As he quickly crossed the trench, he remembered the way the operations sergeant had shurgged his shoulders when the major didn't answer him. It was clear enough to Torres; he was not going to get down on his knees and beg. But now he had some ammunition, and Torres moved quickly through the cutaway path of the protective apron fence. He leaped over and jumped the concertina wires. He moved as fast as he could in the direction of the first building, which was next to his position. He thought the enemy was still regrouping and waiting to continue their attack.

As Torres reached the corner nearest his position, he slowed down, aimed his carbine, and swung it slightly from right to left as he reached the corner of the building. He immediately took a quick look around and saw the enemy soldiers, like scavengers, taking ammunition and equipment from the dead bodies lying around. Torres, without hesitation, came out into the open and, in a frenetic tone, started to spurt fire from his carbine, yelling, "Ungawa, Ungawa, Ungawa."

He had surprised the enemy with his determined assault and screaming. Like a roaring train that can't stop, he fired a burst that dropped nine of the surprised guerrillas. They immediately scattered in all directions, like a flock of birds that had been resting in a bush when someone came along and threw a rock at them. Many started to run into the open rice paddies. Torres saw he was no longer alone. Two young soldiers were moving along with him to his left flank. One of them yelled, "Co-Van number one, Co-Van number one."

"Cam on, Binshi, Cam on, Binshi," Torres answered ("Thank you, soldier").

The young soldiers took positions and continued to fire at the fleeing enemy, who had scattered all over the front and flanks. Torres moved to his old position and started to spot targets at random. He saw a rifle and a man taking aim in his direction. Immediately Torres aimed and fired his weapon, using the sights for the first time. He did not want to miss. The guerrilla went down.

It was a relief when he heard the roaring of flying craft at a distance. Two Huey choppers were moving over Highway 1 in a sweeping motion; their deadly guns were spraying the huge rice plantation to his front. One of them was moving in his direction. Rockets from the side-mounted launchers hit enemy pockets.

The chopper kept flying. Torres looked up and the left gunner of the flying machine recognized that Torres was part of the friendly forces and abstained from delivering fire at his position, Torres, in appreciation, lifted his right arm, and with a gesture of gratitude, raised his thumb with a clenched fist. The young gunner acknowledged the message; clenching his fist, he shook his head up and down and put his thumb up. The pilot of the craft ducked the machine slightly and Torres continued to give his sign of appreciation, opening his palm and waving good-bye to the men as they continued strafing the fields. They aimed at a distant wooded patch that was like an island, discharging their rockets, which ripped and cut down coconut palms and other trees.

The firing continued and many more soldiers came over and started to move to the open field. Four of them reached the position where the guerrilla had been aiming at Torres. They lifted the body and started to carry him back. He was wounded only in his left arm, which was dangling from his shoulder; Torres's aim had been very accurate. They moved the wounded man back, with the intention of giving him aid and getting some information. Torres recognized one of the soldiers carrying the wounded man; he was in charge of the detail.

Well, everything seemed to be under control and Torres's

thoughts were that maybe he might be needed to help rout the infiltrators. He could give a hand if needed. What the heck! After everything else, the worst was probably over.

Torres walked back quickly, following the same path, and saw that Lieutenant Tuck's body was wrapped from head to toe in the blanket he had used to keep him out of shock. Torres raised the blanket slightly and saw the body was lifeless. He kneeled on his left knee and made the sign of the cross, saying, "Rest in peace, Lieutenant Tuck."

Torres walked back to the bunker, where the officers had been. The fortified structure was empty; there were no soldiers, officers, or even ammunition! He walked back toward the hallway of the prison; as he entered the aisle, he saw Lieutenant McDuffie, Captain Johnson, Lieutenant Thiem, and the operations sergeant standing by in front of the first room to the left in the east wing. Major Lang was sitting with an expression of happiness on his face; next to him were two members of the staff taking notes. The two young soldiers who had helped Torres after he started his assault came over and said, "Co-Van Torres number one."

The major said, "Okay, we'll recommend him for a decoration."

The young soldiers once more said, "Beaucoup VCs Nhieu VC chet" ("Many Vietcong are dead").

The captain said, "Alright. Torres, write down what you did and give it to me. I'll send the papers."

Torres did not say a word. He still felt it was not over, yet here people were thinking about decorations. Suddenly Lieutenant McDuffie asked Torres, "Who sent you out there?"

Though Torres could answer, he did not want to offend anyone and decided he'd better move and check around to see if anything else could be done. When Torres did not answer, the young officer said, "Let's recommend him for a Bronze Star."

The captain once more said, "Alright. Write everything down, Sergeant Torres, and I'll fill out the paperwork."

Torres walked away and headed for the jail's front gate, where some members of the battalion had gathered and an ambulance jeep with litters was standing by.

As Torres walked out of the gate, he saw the sergeant in charge of the detail carrying a Vietcong Torres had wounded from the field. The man was breathing heavily, with his eyes open. A first-aid man, leaning on his knees, pulled out a canteen and moistened the young man's lips. Then he shook his head.

Torres moved closer to the dying man. He could not have had a bigger surprise. Just like Ben Hur when he saw Christ carrying the cross, he could not abstain himself and said, "I know this boy. He sold us Cokes two days ago right here."

Sergeant Fong, who also was nearby but had not noticed Torres, came over and said, "Yes, Co-Van, he was a VC."

The dying man looked up with his glassy eyes and, with an expression of forgiveness or compassion, closed them and stopped breathing; he was dead. A medic took a military poncho and covered his body.

Torres decided to walk down the road toward District Headquarters. Just as he was almost halfway there he saw Gunny Tim coming his way. "What's up, Gunny? How are things back there?"

"Not bad, but the VC are inside District Headquarters. The Vietnamese Military Police are trying to get them out. I think they're about done."

Torres asked, "What about the other places?"

"Everything seems to be under control. I'm going back to join the captain. I'll see you."

"Okay, Gunny, take care. I need more ammunition and grenades. I don't have too much left, except a pistol clip full and one carbine magazine. I'll see you."

Both men continued on their respective ways.

As Torres approached District Headquarters, he saw some members of the Vietnamese Military Police and walked over to find out about Gunny's information, although he did not want to get involved unless there was a dire necessity.

"Chao, Sergeant," he greeted a police sergeant.

"Chao, Co-Van."

The sergeant said in English, "VC dead inside on second floor. You can go and see. They made writing on glass of door."

Curious, Torres wanted to check out the sergeant's statement. He walked up to the side door of the building, and the sergeant followed him. As they reached the second floor, on the front of two huge glass doors was a message written in blood, apparently from one of the men.

"Sergeant, what did they write?"

"Co-Van, the man wrote 'Long Live Ho Chi Minh.' Even in death some men send messages. They sure believe in their cause. Someday this war will be over."

"I hope soon, Sergeant. Thank you for the information. Take care of yourself and good luck."

"Thank you, Co-Van."

Torres left the building and continued walking toward the storage room to get some of the supplies he needed. When he returned to the political jail grounds, the word was that the battalion would remain in the area and be ready for another offensive in case the Vietcong had plans to return. Everyone was expecting more action. Torres, the team, and the battalion staff went to stay inside the political jail as before. They would be in there for at least two or three more days.

A report came in that an all-out attack by the North Vietnamese forces and Vietcong guerrillas had been staged throughout the country, and they had failed. Thousands of men from the enemy's forces had died. Complete hamlets were destroyed, but their infrastructure remained intact. There were some sporadic attacks in some areas following the Tet Offensive. There were no major successes, but they wanted to show they were going to be active, as always.

21

The battalion continued their passive defensive role around Quang Tin province. On the 20th of February, the commanders received word that another American-Vietnamese joint operation was being planned.

There was a huge abandoned plantation north of Tam-Ky in the forest, known as the Pineapple Forest. For years attacks had been launched against American and Vietnamese forces from the forest. The area was about 2.3 million square meters, with trees and underbrush. Engineering units from both armies, ripping with bulldozers, tanks, and armored personnel carriers, would move in. The carriers and tanks would move the troops, while the dozers would flatten the ground, destroying foxholes and tunnel complexes. The expectation was that at least 333,000 square yards would be cleared per day. Some of the terrain features were identified by American names—Two Finger Ridge, Charles Hill, among others. They area was crawling with tunnels. The U.S. Marines would also be part of the operation, working with their engineering equipment. Units giving support in case artillery was needed would also accompany the troops. It was going to be a truly combined effort by all the units involved. Air support was also going to be available. The 5th ARVN Regiment were moving in, and the 4th Battalion, as part of it, would be clearing tunnels and booby traps ahead of the bulldozers. The troops would move by carriers, which could provide security to the working crews flattening the area.

Torres received orders from Lieutenant Gatlin, who was the

assistant team commander, as Lieutenant McDuffie was the group commander now and Major Johnson had been promoted and moved to another job elsewhere.

"Sergeant Torres, you will be attached to a Vietnamese rifle platoon. You will accompany them on individual missions; they will be supported by American armored units. If there is need for the tanks to fire at any given target, you will act as coordinator between the platoon leader and the tank commanders. The platoon will be riding the tanks; when they dismount, you will move with them," the lieutenant said, finishing his briefing.

"Alright, sir. I'll do whatever has to be done."

Torres wondered why he had to go alone, although he remembered that he had been in the same situation before and had not objected to the orders.

"Also, I have to tell you, Sergeant Torres, that very shortly you may be moving to Quang Ngai to take the job as the resupply NCO. This may be your last mission out in the field with the battalion."

"Umph! I'd better play it safe and take care of myself a little bit better," Torres stated. "I'm getting shorter by the minute," he concluded.

Before the Pineapple Forest Operation was due to start, Torres had to accompany Lieutenant Gatlin to Field Regimental Command Headquarters to get maps of the area and receive other instructions. The lieutenant drove the jeep, with Torres at his side.

The 5th Regimental Command Headquarters was located southwest of Pineapple Forest and 6,500 yards east of Route 1. Lieutenant Gatlin received orders to report there and pick up maps and orders related to the operation. Torres got called and the lieutenant said to him, "Sergeant Torres, you will go with me to the OP, where Regimental Headquarters is. I have to pick up maps and receive instructions. We'll ride in the jeep, and you may pick up anything you need at the storage room later. We'll stop there after."

Torres answered, "Alright, sir. I'm ready to go anytime."

Fifteen minutes later the two men departed and the lieutenant at the driving wheel veered the vehicle off to the hill, which was five hundred meters above sea level, where Regimental Headquarters was located.

The jeep entered the fenced perimeter, where the bunkers gave the appearance of an Old West wagon train as it formed a circle to fight an Indian assault. The command bunker was located to the north and could be distinguished from the others by the huge antennas for radio communication on top of it. It was also the largest and biggest structure inside the perimeter.

When the jeep reached the hill and the lieutenant had parked near one of the bunkers located to the right of the command bunker, Torres saw two advisors walking toward a jeep parked nearby. The two men had walked out of the command bunker. Torres immediately recognized them. As the lieutenant went up to the huge structure, Torres quickly walked up to them and said, "Hello there! It's been a long time since I've seen you guys. I thought you left me here and were already on the other side."

The two sergeants, recognizing Torres, greeted him very cheerfully, "Gosh!" said Oshiro, "and I thought with what I heard about you, and what you did in Tet, you were working in some headquarters. How are things, pal?" he asked.

"Well, not bad, I think my time is coming up and I'll be going somewhere else soon. It's been a very long six months. How about you, Phillips? I haven't seen you since school days at Bragg. I knew you were coming this way."

"Well, Buddy, I'm with this Nip here riding the cavalry also. I came about a week after you guys got here. I know about your old buddy, Hicks. What a shame."

Torres said, "That's the way things are. I've had many close calls, but it seems like it's not my time yet. I may get back home and get splattered by a trailer in the middle of a road, and here there's a hail of flying bullets and, thanks to the Good Lord, none of them have touched me."

As the men talked, a Huey helicopter landed nearby at a pad located in the southwest area of the OP. It had circled around twice over the men's heads.

"Umph! It looks like some big wheel is coming," said Torres.

Oshiro immediately said, "Oh, yeah! I just heard that a retired field marshall from the British army is coming. He'll be gathering some information for a book he's writing."

Torres snapped back, "I bet you, my friend, that this fellow gets here and leaves in less than ten minutes. He'll hear what they want to tell him and he'll snap some pictures of those poor fellows blindfolded over there. He'll jump back into the chopper and move out. You know these guys. If they want to see the real war, they should come and stay over here for at least a couple of days. These guys go back and write best sellers and talk about the war when they don't know what's going on."

Torres pointed to four suspects who were kneeling in front of the command bunker. Two were women and two were men. They were dressed in black pajamas and were guarded by two soldiers.

Oshiro and Phillips looked over. With Torres they saw a tall, lean man step out of the Huey. He had a figure similar to that of General Montgomery, as portrayed in films. Dressed in clear khaki clothes, as if he were going on safari, and holding a swagger stick in his hands and a small camera slung around and to the left of his waist, he walked along, taking long strides. An officer from the command bunker walked over and saluted him. Using gestures, he guided the visiting gentleman to the command bunker. The marshall took a quick glance at the four kneeling suspects before he entered the bunker.

Torres and his two friends kept talking about the operation at Pineapple Forest.

"Torres, you take care of yourself. I wish you could ride

with me; my APC offers better protection."

"Yes, Oshiro, but when you're out there, you guys already know nothing is safe. You two take care of yourselves."

As Torres was talking, the visiting marshall walked out of the bunker, pulled out his camera, and snapped two pictures of the four blindfolded, barefooted, and trembling figures, who did not know what was going on.

Phillips said, "You were right, Torres. How did you know he was going to take pictures and walk out so fast?"

"Listen, Phillips and Oshiro, and know this. If you go to Disneyworld and don't take a camera and take pictures, nobody is going to believe you were there. Simple as that. Show the world you were there, even if you can't shake hands with Mickey Mouse and Goofy and all of the other characters. It's like that."

Oshiro said, "I'm glad to see you; maybe we'll see each other sometimes. We have to go now to get ready for this operation. Don't forget to write home. I do it every time I get the chance."

Torres said, "Good-bye, guys, and good luck. I hope to see you around. I remember, I once heard a saying I've never forgotten. What did the rabbi say to the young man after the circumcision?"

"What did he say, Torres?" asked Oshiro.

"It won't be too long now. It won't be too long now."

Torres waved his right arm at them, as they rode down the hill to join their unit.

Lieutenant Gatlin came out of the command bunker and Torres said, "Well, I just met some of my buddies and talked to them. They're with the armored units and they'll be together in the Pineapple Forest Operation. Sir, did you see that man who came to get information for a book he's writing?

"Is that what he came for?" the lieutenant asked.

"Yeah. He looks like he was ready for a fox chase with his hat and swagger stick made of leather, spit-polished boots, and a camera. He should be in Hollywood."

The lieutenant didn't say anything as the jeep rode down the hill and entered the main highway toward Tam-Ky.

"Sergeant Torres, tonight we'll be staying with members of the Marine engineering units who are going to be involved in the operation. The ARVN units, along with our battalion, will be deployed around and will provide security. We can eat with the American units and use our air mattresses. They'll be forward observers in case we need artillery support and some illumination around the area. This may be your last operation in the field. You'll probably be moved to Quang Ngai to take a job at the compound there very soon. You have almost six months working with the units in the field. Sometime in the future, I'll get a job somewhere too when I get my six months. I have only two here."

The two men went to the Vietnamese compound and picked up rations, clean clothes, and other necessary equipment they needed. Immediately after, they drove up to where the battalion was. It was deployed north of Tam-Ky and very near the political jail.

Early the next morning the battalion moved and the advisory team rode up and joined the American forces. They were deployed along the ridge line southeast of Pineapple Forest and northwest of Regimental Headquarters.

22

The day passed without incidence, and the commanders worked on the coordination for the operation. The day was very placid, and in the evening, at 1800 hours, the hot meal for the engineering units came in. It was delivered by choppers. Torres talked with some of the guys as they shared their food with him.

Torres dug a foxhole near one of the canvas tents and inflated his air mattress. He was ready for the night and was more at ease and relaxed, as he was with an American unit. He was not going to take anything for granted, but it was just a matter of thinking that if something happened and he needed support, he would be more than likely to get it.

Bulldozers were parked and tanks were deployed around the area, as well as other armored units. The Vietnamese units were deployed around the area also, located mostly to the north and west of Torres's location.

The night approached and once in a while some artillery flares illuminated the skies. Some of the American staff members were sleeping in cots under the canvas tents.

At 2200 hours sounds of small-arms firing broke the monotony of the night. A message was received that ARVN units located to the north and very visible from Torres's location had come under ground attack. A request for artillery support came in, and the forward observer plotted the coordinates on a map. An artillery barrage was fired. Torres could see very clearly as the explosions ripped the ground about 1,100 yards to the north of his position. Suddenly someone yelled, "Cease fire! Cease fire! Those are friendly positions. Everything is okay. There is no attack."

The result of the error was four Vietnamese soldiers killed and six wounded. *As in every war*, Torres thought. *Friendly fire!*

The next day Torres was called in by Lieutenant McDuffie and told, "Sergeant Torres, you will be riding with a Vietnamese platoon. Your job will be coordinator and interpreter if the need for tank or artillery support arises. The platoon will be mounted on top of the tanks. You know that every tank has a radio to communicate with the crew inside. Be careful and do not take any unnecessary chances."

Torres felt apprehensive, but he was not going to question the order. He would be by himself and alone with a rifle platoon. He expected that the platoon would get out of the tank now and then and clear areas and foxholes along the way. The tank would be standing by, ready to give support if needed. The bulldozers would be dispersed not far behind, smashing and uprooting trees all over. Helicopters with gunners managing .30-caliber machine guns and rockets would be circling the area up in the air. Observation planes would also be in the air.

Torres knew about some of the jobs done by the famous Tunnel Rats of Cuchi in the south. He had his gas mask ready and four tear gas grenades just in case he had to use them.

The platoon mounted four tanks, one squad per each tank, as the soldiers hung from the steel-crossed rods around the commander turret and to the top rear of it. Torres secured himself, with his left hand holding a step bar on the right of the turret of the ninety-ton monster. The young platoon leader was on the left side. Torres held his carbine at the small of the stock, his index finger off the trigger. The safety latch was on, and no bayonet was attached to his carbine.

The armored unit moved quickly up and down ravines and

crossed ditches, squashing pineapple plants growing wild under the weight of the armored monsters. There was no sign of any guerrillas, and with tanks roaring and swinging their 90-mm guns in each of them, no enemy was going to stand idle and wait to be run over or be blown to pieces.

The tanks stopped about 250 yards before reaching the foot of a hill that extended from north to south. Torres received word from the tank's commander to relay the order to the Vietnamese platoon leader and told him what he was supposed to do with the platoon.

"Sarge, tell the lieutenant to dismount his platoon and clear the area. We can't move forward until they do that."

"Alright, sir. I'll tell him right away."

Some soldiers had already jumped off the vehicle and taken prone positions facing the hill. Apparently, they did not want to be hit by snipers that might be watching the troop movement from the hills.

Torres yelled to the young Vietnamese lieutenant, "Thieu Uy, Lam cho, cach cham" ("Dismount quickly").

The lieutenant understood what Torres had said and proceeded to jump off immediately, while Torres did the same. The lieutenant gave a command to his platoon to align and move forward.

Some weapon firing was heard coming from adjacent areas to the right and left of the platoon. The troops walked forward and watched the ground they were walking on closely. Torres was doing the same as everyone else, aware that land mines and booby traps could have been planted by the Vietcong anticipating the actions of the troops involved in the operation.

The platoon line reached an area about four hundred yards from the hill's base. Half-concealed tunnels and foxholes could be clearly seen located along the hill and the base. The sporadic vegetation made it difficult to distinguish clearly some of the entrances to the caves. All along the hill there were half-dried trees and bushes with a yellowish color, as a result of the chemicals and bombs that had exploded in the air before hitting the ground. Some of the branches of the trees resembled weeping willows, their leaves hanging perpendicular to the ground. Some of them were as high as a hundred feet or more and had the appearance of being standing Goliaths defeated by an invisible David, their branches, like fallen arms, dangling. Almost everywhere the vegetation's appearance was identical.

The platoon moved at a steady pace toward the hill's base. Torres was at the right flank with the leader of the squad assigned to cover the sector. The platoon leader was continuously moving from right to left and pushing some of the soldiers. He had been doing the same from the time the troops dismounted the tanks. The vehicles followed slowly behind and then stopped at a distance of two hundred yards away from the hill's base.

By leaps and bounds the soldiers moved until they had reached the base of the hill. Some of the soldiers stood by the sides of the tunnels when they neared them. The tunnel's entrances were in a rounded shape and high and wide enough to accommodate a pair of men five feet tall, walking side by side. Torres thought that for him to walk in, he would have to bend from his waist. He was six feet tall in his bare feet and at least three to four inches more with his helmet and jungle boots on.

The squad that Torres was with dispersed along and near two tunnels that were about fifty feet apart. Torres waited to see if any of the soldiers were going to check them inside. He was near the extreme right. The cave near him was five yards away.

The squad leader did not give any order. Torres motioned to him that he was going to help as he drew near the cave's entrance. He quickly took a fast glance inside and rapidly withdrew his head, well aware that someone might take a potshot at him. He did not want to have his head blown off by anybody inside. Torres yelled in his basic Vietnamese, "Di di oday, Chac cham Ong." He was trying to tell anyone inside the cave to come outside fast.

The squad leader, getting the idea from Torres, started to speak loudly in Vietnamese. Someone responded from inside. Torres leaned his carbine against the side of the cave and took his pack off. He pulled his pistol from his shoulder holster. He cocked it and took the safety latch off. He reached for a flashlight and extracted it from a small pouch on the right side of his H-frame pack. He lit it and checked to see that it worked.

Torres slowly focused the light of the flashlight inside the cave and saw that the cave was not as deep as he'd anticipated; it went only about fifteen yards into the hillside. He saw two figures in crouched positions at the farthest end. Torres did not aim his pistol directly at any of them but held it high, pointing it upward. He knew he could use the quick kill action. He walked slowly into the cave, saying, "Toi Bac Mi. Nihu ong oday, Di Di oday" ("I am American. Men, come here. Come here").

The two men apparently understood what Torres meant. They stood up slowly and walked forward in a very apprehensive manner. They bowed in sign of respect, holding the palms of their hands together as people do while praying and doing reverence.

The squad leader called over two of his men as soon as Torres and the prisoners were out of the cave. He ordered the two soldiers to escort the suspects to the rear to be interrogated. The soldiers next to the other cave started to check the tunnel. They did not find anyone. Torres was pleased that they yelled and called out to anyone who might be inside first. They did not throw grenades, and they used flashlights. Each squad leader carried one.

After Torres saw the two men being taken away, the squad leader said to him, "Co-Van, number one."

"Cam on, Trung Si." Torres thanked him for his statement. He did not want to see some innocent peasant get shot unnecessarily, and he had succeeded.

The squad moved and Torres heard some loud talk coming

from his right flank. He noticed that another platoon was moving along and had taken up a position along the hill's ridge line.

He walked over and approached a soldier, at the same time hoping he could understand. He asked, "Bac mi Co-Van odau?" ("Where is the American advisor?") The soldier pointed to his right, where loud voices could be heard.

Torres walked slowly and carefully to prevent stepping on any mine or booby trap that might be in the area. There were numerous ridges and ravines, and vegetation was very dense in some spots.

He neared some dispersed trees and used them to hold himself and prevent sliding down the cliffs, which had a 55- to 60-degree angle. He stopped suddenly when he saw some men talking in English and others giving commands in Vietnamese. Torres knew that something was going on when he saw an American officer pointing to two men dressed in black pajamas, their hands tied in front of them. They had their arms locked by a piece of wood placed between their backs and the bends of their elbows. They were not blindfolded, and their heads were lowered.

Torres watched the two soldiers move the prisoners and tie them to two trees ten feet apart. The soldiers placed a thin rope around their waists and the trees. They also tied them up by their necks around the trees. The men could not bring their heads down as they were tied by the upper part of their neck.

The American officer walked away, making a statement about bringing the prisoners to the rear to be interrogated. A Vietnamese captain, who was the officer talking in English to the American officer, left with him. Torres continued to watch and saw a Vietnamese lieutenant walk over and close in on the two prisoners. He said something that Torres could not understand because of the distance and the fast talk. The two men shook their heads in a sign of denial. They were crying and very afraid.

The officer stepped back and walked away, after calling a sergeant. He said something in the sergeant's left ear. The sergeant nodded his head in an affirmative gesture. All of the officers had gone and were out of sight when Torres saw the sergeant take a rifle from one of the soldiers who had helped tie up the prisoners. The sergeant aimed the rifle in a menacing way toward the two prisoners. He was only ten feet away. Torres quickly walked down. At the same time the sergeant fired, the bullet hitting the prisoner on the right in his left ear lobe, almost blowing the ear away.

Immediately Torres reached the area and asked the sergeant, as he stepped in front of the tied prisoners, "Tai sao, Trung Si?" ("Why, Sergeant?")

The sergeant said, "I only wanted to scare them and the rifle fired."

Torres looked at him. The sergeant did not look back, but he walked over and told the soldiers to take the two prisoners to the rear. The man with the shot ear was in a daze. Torres took off his first-aid pack and tied a bandage around the man's head. He hoped that the bandage would do the job as the wound seemed to be superficial and was not bleeding profusely. The man did not go into shock, but he was dazed and crying.

The soldiers guided the two prisoners back, walking up the small hill in the same direction that the others had gone before. The sergeant followed, Torres behind. They reached the rear command and the prisoners were assisted by first-aid men. The sergeant talked to the captain and told him that his weapon had malfunctioned and a shot had gone off unintentionally.

Torres looked down and shook his head. He walked over to the officer and said, "Sir, I am Sergeant Torres, and I work with the 4th Battalion of the 5th Regiment. I don't want to contradict what the sergeant told you, but it is not good to aim a weapon at a suspect, even if he is a Vietcong."

"Sergeant, I told the sergeant to interrogate the prisoner briefly. He is a Vietcong and he is our enemy; they do bad things."

Torres said, "Sir, excuse me, but are we any better if we do things like that? We must treat people right. No Vietcong is going to lay down his arms and turn himself in if the soldiers continue to do things like that. You'll never win."

"I know, Co-Van. I must go now. I guarantee you that it will never happen again."

"I hope not, sir. Thank you for listening."

Torres saluted him; then, before walking away, he said, "Chao Dai Uy" ("Good-bye, Captain").

"Chao, Trung Si Nhut Torres" ("Good-bye, Sergeant First Class Torres").

23

Torres walked back to the Operations Headquarters command area and joined his team. He received instructions to be ready for a short operation, which was to start the next day. The battalion would do a mop-up operation along the seashore northeast of Tam-Ky. The mission was to clear the area of some suspected Vietcong who had moved from Pineapple Forest, evading the combined operations forces. They had dispersed along the marshes and hamlets near the Yellow Sea. The team would be complete, moving with the battalion staff as they normally did.

The battalion plans were outlined. The commander called his staff and company commanders. He assigned sectors to each company and the direction of movement for each unit. The battalion would cross the highway ten miles north of the capital city, while moving in an easterly direction. After crossing the highway and once the leading elements reached the shoreline, the whole battalion would swing south and check the fields, marshes, hamlets, and/or any other suspected area where Vietcong could be hiding.

At 0700 hours, the battalion was ready to move, and Torres thought that maybe it would be his last time out in the field. He would then be going to work at a desk job somewhere. Lieutenant Gatlin said, "Well, Sergeant Torres, are you happy this may be it for you?"

Torres answered, "In some ways, yes. I hope things get better and the war ends soon."

"Everyone hopes for the same," the lieutenant stated.

The battalion moved slowly. There were sugar-cane patches, many ditches, rice paddies as usual, and marshes. The leading units reached the seashore by 1150 hours. The battalion staff moved forward and joined them; then the whole battalion started to move south as planned. The staff followed the rifle platoon deployed close to the shore. The staff was only 150 yards behind.

The battalion commander gave orders to stop and take time to eat lunch. Some small hamlets had been searched along the way. The residents were fishermen and their families. There were boats and small rafts pulled up from the water and secured to pickets by short ropes. Fishing nets were hanging from picket lines. Normally the fishermen hang them out to dry and make repairs. Some nets could be seen strung out in the water at various distances. There were no boats in sight, either sailing or tending to the nets.

The battalion staff stopped after passing a small hamlet that had only about ten dispersed hootches. The families were small in size, varying from four to six people; mostly they were children. There were only three or four old men; by their appearances, their fishing days had long gone. They were sitting around, smoking pipes and looking out to sea. It appeared as if they were longing for the days when they used to sail out and bring in a big or small catch but without the risk of getting stopped by a speedy shore patrol boat. Gone were those days.

Corporal Tiep had purchased some fish and was starting to prepare the staff's lunch. It would be rice and fish. Some vegetables would be boiled and a stew would be prepared. Tiep had unhooked his pack with the pots and pans, with some help from another soldier, who had also helped carry pots and pans. The corporal began his chores. He had a fish that weighed about fifteen pounds. He scaled it and cut its belly to pull out the fish guts, which were sizable. Meanwhile, Torres looked for a spot to eat. Finding one, he pulled a can of corned beef hash out and, with a heating tablet, warmed it. He also prepared some cocoa in his canteen cup.

After warming his meal, Torres looked for a spot to sit and lean back. There it was! A huge coconut tree. He looked up to check that no dried coconuts were hanging up at the top. He remembered a story one of his brothers-in-law told of a nephew who'd gotten knocked out by a dried coconut that fell on his head. The poor fellow walked around in a daze for a couple of weeks, all the time asking, "When did I join the navy?" He had to wear a bandage around his head.

After Torres sat down, Corporal Tiep came over and asked, "Co-Van, muon canh? Canh rau number one."

"Sure, Corporal. I like it."

The corporal walked back and brought Torres a bowl of hot soup.

"Number one soup, Co-Van."

Torres smilingly said, "Thank you, Tiep. Thank you very much."

The almost boiling broth looked like Campbell's clam chowder. He took a couple of crackers and dropped them into the bowl after crumbing them into pieces. Once in a while Torres glanced up to check the coconut tree and hoped that no rat fell off. He stopped worrying about falling coconuts.

Torres enjoyed his soup very much. It ran smoothly down his throat. The vegetables were all ground down, and the rice was pulverized. The taste could rival the soups created by the best chefs.

Torres finished his meal and brought the empty bowl back to Tiep. "Number one, Tiep. I loved it." He walked back and saw Lieutenant Thiem, who also finished eating his soup.

"Hi, Co-Van. You like Tiep's food, eh? I heard you. You said it was number one."

"It sure was. He put clams in it; it went down very smoothly."

"You know, Co-Van. You like Vietnamese food. Maybe when you get back, you'll tell people to eat it. It's the best soup in the world, the one we just ate—fish guts."

"Fish guts?" Torres snapped back.

"Yes, Co-Van, fish guts. Corporal Tiep cleaned them and made number one soup."

"Thank you, Lieutenant. I should not have asked."

"Why, Co-Van? It is okay if you ask me."

"It's of no use now. It's already down the hatch."

"What do you mean, Co-Van."

"Nothing, sir. Nothing."

Torres walked back to the coconut palm and said to Lieutenant Gatlin, who was nearby, "I'm not taking any chances, even if this coconut palm doesn't have any coconuts hanging up there."

"Sergeant, you've been under that tree for a half hour and no coconut has fallen on you up to now."

"Well, anyway, I'm not going to take any chances, as I said. The damned thing may want to get rewarded by the Vietcong and quickly grow a coconut and drop it on my head. I may be hardheaded, but I'd better play it safe with the things that happen around here, Lieutenant."

The battalion got ready to move and continued in a southerly direction. The unit had been checking the immediate areas and not many soldiers walked by the white sands close to the water. There were some boats upside down, resting flat on the sand; others were resting over built-up log frames. The leader of the platoon nearest to the sea sent soldiers to check the boats. It was not too great a surprise to find some Vietcong suspects hidden under them.

The soldiers turned over the boats that were on the log frames; the suspects were clinging to the undersides. They had their feet tied to the bottom of the boats and they held themselves up with their hands, their faces looking toward the ground. Some speed boats were constantly patrolling the off-shore area. As the unit moved on, they kept abreast.

At 1500 hours, small-arms firing could be heard from the platoon, and Lieutenant Gatlin ran up to check. Everyone dispersed quickly and took to the ground. Torres looked up to see what was going on. The firing intensified and it appeared that a sizable Vietcong force had been located and engaged. Torres did not see any bullets hitting around his area, and neither did he hear any zooming of projectiles over or near his head. He could recognize from his experience the proximity of any flying projectile or missile. He thought that perhaps the enemy was being routed and was on the run.

Torres got up and moved forward to check. He advanced by leaps and bounds for two hundred yards until he came in view of Lieutenant Gatlin, who was in a prone position behind a rice paddy embankment. He was firing his rifle along with some soldiers. Torres could not make out the targets they were trying to knock out or keep pinned down. The firing slowed.

Torres walked closer to the lieutenant, who yelled, "VC."

Torres kept trying to locate them, realizing that this should be easy for him. The area to the front was sandy and clear of obstacles. There were no ditches except for small sand dunes no more than six inches in height. He checked the water, always maintaining a low silhouette for safety purposes.

The firing of weapons slowed to three to four rounds per second, and Torres slowly stood up; then he recognized the intended targets. He could see bullets striking the water at a distance of 150 yards from the shore. There were no boats except for two South Vietnamese speed boats patrolling the shores. They were about 500 yards to the south of the target.

By instinct, Torres walked up to the front of the prone soldiers and said once more, as he had before, "Khong kiet!" ("Do not fire"). Torres could see at a distance two floating bodies. The waves lifted them. Red spots were clearly visible from the shore as the boats neared them.

The boats did not pick them up, indicating there was no need to haul them aboard and take them prisoner; the sharks could feast on them. Torres thought that perhaps it had been unnecessary to fire at them, but it was too late. The patrol boats would have captured them; there was no escape. Now nobody would knew whether they were foe or friend, fleeing in panic and afraid of the advancing troops.

The operation ended a short time later as the troops closed in on the city. The battalion was ordered to move to the same area where the unit was at Tet. The staff was quartered in two buildings reinforced with sand bags around. Sleeping cots were brought for the staff officers and the advisory team.

Torres inflated his air mattress and placed it on top of his cot. He felt tired and wanted to rest in a softer bed. It was not going to be too long before he would be leaving and going elsewhere to complete his tour.

24

Early the next morning, Torres got up. After brushing his teeth and washing his face, he was called by Lieutenant Gatlin.

"This is it, Sergeant Torres. You'll make first sergeant very shortly. You're already on the promotion list, as I probably told you before."

"Yes, Lieutenant, I know. Maybe by the time I get home I'll have my new rank on my lapel. I'll be behind a desk administrating a basic training company. I hope to go back to Dix in New Jersey; I liked it there. I could bring my family, and my kids could go to school there."

"Well, Sergeant, I have good news for you. Today you'll be leaving for good. The resupply chopper will pick you up at 1300 hours. Be ready. Go pick up your stuff at the storage room; the jeep will bring you back. If you want, you can wait for it, and it will also take you there."

"No, sir. I'll walk. It will do me good. The jeep can bring me back. Just send it for me about one hour after I leave. It's not that far. I've walked it before, and it only takes ten minutes. The fresh air will do me good."

"Okay, Sarge. I'll send the jeep for you. Just get ready and don't forget anything."

Lieutenant Theim was listening to the conversation between Torres and the lieutenant. He shook his head slightly. He looked both resigned and appreciative. He knew he was going to miss a friend, but he was happy that Torres was going back safe to join his family, or at least he was going to be in a safer place until he did. He thought he would talk to Torres later before his departure.

The word got around that Co-Van Torres was leaving. Torres walked down the dirt road, many memories flooding his mind. He was happy he was leaving, but he felt sad for those he was leaving behind. He walked slowly but with his head up. As he reached the entrance to the Vietnamese compound, he saw a girl and a boy about nine years old each. Immediately he stopped and dropped his pack. He opened the straps of a pocket and, without saying a word, handed the last of his candy to the children. The kids looked at each other and with radiant faces smiled and bowed their heads, as Torres lifted his pack and walked away. He was only two hundred yards from the storage room.

An hour later the quarter-ton truck driven by Sergeant Fong came over to pick Torres up. He had everything packed and ready to go. It was only a matter of hours before he would be flying back, following almost the same route he had flown when he'd first arrived at the observation post and been greeted by Hoi, the houseboy, as he was identified by the staff and the team.

It was 1100 hours and they seemed long. Torres walked out of the building, after resting on his cot for a while. Somebody would be using it later and there was no need to fold it. As he stepped out the door, Theim approached him and said, "Co-Van Torres, I have to tell you that we will miss you. Many months ago I told you that you would make many friends, more than enemies. I am glad that you are going home safe. I will not forget you. By the way, I made first lieutenant yesterday."

"Thank you, Trung Uy. No more Thieu Uy. I'm happy for you. I hope you get to see your family soon. I hope the war ends and peace comes to Vietnam. You'll be remembered by me always. Keep your head down, as we say in America. Thanks for your confidence and friendship."

"Okay, Trung Si Torres. If you don't mind, Corporal Tiep wants to see you before you go. Please go over there. He is in that small canvas tent."

"Okay, sir. I'll go now."

Corporal Tiep was standing by entrance to the small canvas tent. When Torres neared him, he placed his left hand on Torres's right arm and guided him inside the tent. Torres, looking at the floor, saw a white cloth spread on the ground, a covered plate in the center. It was covered with a piece of cloth slightly larger than a man's handkerchief. There were chopsticks by the side.

"Please sit down, Co-Van."

Torres sat, crossing his legs in the customary Oriental way. Corporal Tiep sat across from him. "Co-Van, I don't know if I am happy or sad because you are going home. You are my friend and everyone likes you. I am sorry I could not do better with the food I prepared for you. Maybe I will see you later, and it will be better."

"It is okay, Hasi. You will always be in my heart as a good friend. People here are very nice, and I hope the war finishes and you can live in peace with your family."

Corporal Tiep took the cover of the dish off. Torres looked at the tiny fried objects. He felt honored by the corporal's actions. On the plate were nine small sparrows with their heads on. He had to eat at least half of them; five of them would do it. He reached for the chopsticks and holding the first one between their tips, be brought it to his mouth and bit off the sparrow head quickly, swallowing it. He repeated this four more times; then he pointed with his left hand and an open upward palm to Corporal Tiep. Bowing his head, he indicated to the corporal to eat the others.

Tiep said, "Thank you, Co-Van," and proceeded to eat the rest, smiling happily and saying, "Number one, Co-Van. Number one."

After the meal Torres got up. Tiep reached into the right

pocket of his fatigue jacket. He extracted a small homemade pipe that he used. It was made of copper and could be disassembled into three pieces for cleaning. He handed it to Torres and said, "Take this pipe, Co-Van. It is for you. You can smoke. Break your cigarettes and put the tobacco in it."

"Thank you, Corporal Tiep. I want you to buy something for your kids when you go home next time." He pulled his wallet out and extracted a one-thousand-piaster bill, which he handed to Tiep.

"Thank you one more time, Co-Van." Tears poured down Tiep's wrinkled face. Torres then shook hands, bowed, and said, "Good-bye, my friend." He walked out of the tent, using his handkerchief to wipe his own teary eyes.

The Huey aircraft arrived on time. The expressions on many faces were of sadness and consolation. Sergeant Fong, Hoi, Boom-Boom, and other members of the battalion came over to say good-bye to Da Co-Van Torres. The battalion commander came out of the staff quartering building and gave orders to Lieutenant Bam, the operations officer, to bring a small case.

The operations officer ordered all the Vietnamese soldiers to come to attention. The battalion commander walked up to Torres and, in a surprise action, took the case handed him by Lieutenant Bam and opened it, pulling out a medal. The commander then pinned the medal on the left lapel of Torres's camouflage jacket. The men applauded in a sign of approval. The commander said, "Thank you, Trung Si Nhut Torres. Thank you for your cooperation and assistance. You are a very good person. We will not forget you. Thank you from all of us."

"Sir, I came here to be another Co-Van almost seven months ago. I made many friends, and I'll not forget them either. All of you are good people. They tell us to try to win the minds and hearts of people and all of you have won mine. Good luck to you all, and I hope the war finishes soon and you can live in peace. Thanks for the medal and your words."

Torres gave a military salute and with a sharp cut of his right arm brought it to his side; the commander recognized and returned Torres's salute. It was a short and informal ceremony but very meaningful for everyone there. Torres had been presented with the Gallantry Cross.

The operations officer told one of the sergeants, "Sergeant, give Co-Van Torres the orders for the medal."

The sergeant immediately gave Torres a manila folder, which contained a brief description written in Vietnamese, with an English translation inside. Torres said, "Thank you, Sergeant. Thank you, Lieutenant."

The battalion commander walked back, after shaking Torres's hand, and said, "Good-bye, Sergeant Torres."

Everyone came over to shake hands with Torres, saying "Chao, Co-Van." As they walked away, some of them gave him a military salute.

The chopper had been waiting for almost ten minutes. Torres said, "Now I must go. Chao to all of you."

Hoi walked over, grasped Torres's duffel bag and cargo pack, and walked over to the aircraft, handing it to a machine gunner who secured it aboard the chopper. Torres walked over to the craft. Just before he reached the door, Hoi came over and embraced him, saying, "Chao, Da Co-Van, yes, Co-Van, Da Co-Van Torres. Good luck Trung Si Nhut."

"Good-bye, Hoi, my friend. Good-bye and take care of yourself. Maybe I will come back sometime in the future and see you."

Torres climbed into the helicopter, which immediately started to swing its rotor blades, lifting off the ground in a vertical direction while Torres waved his right arm. The men on the ground reciprocated in the same manner. The chopper swung slightly north and circled once more, then flew in the southerly direction toward Quang Ngai. It followed the same path it had when Torres had first joined the team, but this time he was going back.

The chopper landed at a helipad near the MACV compound. The same driver who had driven Torres when he'd arrived at Quang Ngai had a jeep standing by. He walked over. Recognizing Torres, he said, "Hello, Sergeant Torres. Remember me?"

"Yes, I do. You brought me to the compound from the airport. I'll be working somewhere near here now."

"Yes, I know. You'll be resupply sergeant for Team Two. You won't be going into the field again unless there is an emergency. The job is good, and it's safer at the compound, although the VC got inside the hospital during Tet and took it over. I don't think it will happen to the compound. You'll eat hot meals, take hot showers, and wear clean clothes all the time. You'll see movies and drink a beer at the club. It's like garrison life."

"Thank for the information. What is your name? I never checked your name tag."

"Sterling. Allan Sterling. I don't have too much time left here either. In two months I di di maul, as the Vietnamese say. I get out of here and back to the world."

The two loaded Torres's equipment into the back seat of the jeep and left the helipad, waving to the chopper's crew who took off on another of their routine missions.

As the vehicle approached the compound after a five-minute drive, Sterling asked Torres, "I heard it's rough out there. You probably had many close calls, didn't you?"

"Yes, Sterling, I did. Thanks to the Good Lord, I made it. It was hard sometimes, but I made many friends."

"You'll probably get some kind of medal. You deserve it. You know, I heard sometimes officers write each other for medals. Is that true?"

"I heard that too, Sterling. I don't know, but as they say in Spanish, when you hear the rumble of noise at a river, it is because it is going to increase the water's volume and it will flood all over. I don't like to make a statement without being sure of it, but I've also heard that."

25

The jeep arrived at the compound and parked at the designated spot in front of the orderly room. The driver helped Torres unload his equipment. The first sergeant came out and said to Torres, "Welcome, Sergeant Torres. I'm First Sergeant Baker. I just took this job not so long ago. You'll be the resupply NCO. Your duties are outlined and you can familiarize yourself with them quickly. You have an assistant, Specialist Four Martin. He's also the mail clerk. He'll help you gather up the equipment needed by the troops in the field. The supply sergeant will fill any requests you give him when you get them from the team out in the field. You don't have to fly or ride out there.

"Your room is ready. It's number 15 in the left wing, two doors past the showers. There'll be a housemaid, and you can pay a small fee at the orderly room for having your bed made, washing, and getting your clothes pressed. Don't give anything to any of the women working here. They are mamasans, and they are searched at the gate by the Vietnamese police and the MPs. Anything you give them will be confiscated at the gate, and you may get in trouble."

"Thanks for the information, First Sergeant. I'll try to do my job to the best of my abilities. Thank you for everything."

The first sergeant concluded, "If you need any assistance or have any doubts, come and see me. Specialist Sterling will help you with your stuff. He'll show you the room also."

"Thanks once more, First Sergeant."

Torres picked up his H-frame pack and the bow and arrows

given to him by the Montagnard chief. Sterling picked up the duffel bag and cargo pack. Torres followed him. Both men reached the front door of room 15, where Sterling put the bags down and said to Torres, "Good luck, Sergeant Torres. Don't volunteer for anything. It doesn't pay."

"Thanks, Sterling, for your help, and I know what you mean. Take care. I'll see you around."

"Alright, Sarge," Sterling said, as he walked away, following the same path back to his vehicle to wait for his next orders or to do maintenance on his vehicle.

There were two empty beds in room 15, and Torres chose the first one on the right of the door. There were some wire hangers he could use for his pressed fatigues. A mamasan about fifty years old came over and said, "Sergeant, I will wash your clothes and press them. Just put the dirty clothes on the bed or the floor. I do a good job for you. Me number one. I make your bed also and clean floors. Do not worry; I take care of everything."

"Thank you, Ba."

"Oh! You know Vietnamese."

"No, I know nha Vietnamese. A little only. Toi Da Co-Van Hai Su Doan O La Quang Tin" ("I was advisor of the 2nd Division in Quang Tin province").

"Number one Trung si."

"Thank you, Mamasan."

Torres walked over to the supply room and was given linen. He brought it back and the mamasan made his bed up quickly for him. He then sorted out his clothes, placing the dirty ones by the side on the floor. Mamasan picked them up and walked away to check the other rooms in the same wing.

Torres walked to the resupply sergeant's office. When he entered the opened front door, he was greeted by Specialist Four Martin. "Welcome, Sergeant Torres. I'm specialist Martin, and I'll be your assistant. I'll help you in everything you want me to help you with. I know what to do, and this job is not a hard one. If you get an order, I'll help you fill it. Don't worry. You need the break after being out there in the field. It's like compensatory duty for breaking your ass out there. You deserve it, Sarge. We work from nine to five, unless there's an emergency request. Don't feel bad for having it easy now. Enjoy it while you can before you leave here. You'll meet a lot of your friends who come around here to stay and work in easy jobs."

The months of April and May went by and Torres continued his job filling requests with the help of Martin. Toward the middle of June, as Torres was walking to the mess hall to eat lunch, he stopped and recognized a sergeant he had seen before.

"Hello, Phillips. How are you? How is Oshiro? Have you seen him?"

"Hello, Torres. I'm okay. I'm still working with the armored battalion. As to Oshiro's whereabouts, I can tell you that he's working very near here. You may have seen him."

"No, Phillips. I haven't seen him. Maybe he's been around and I've missed him. I'm the resupply sergeant."

"Yes, I know. I got everything you sent me. I appreciate it. By the way, I heard you were getting some kind of medal. A very high one. It will be presented by a general, so it has to be a big one. I heard it. You probably know of it already."

"As a matter of fact, I didn't know. You're the first one I've heard it from. Well, whatever they give me is fine if it's based on true facts. I think I did my job out there. I wish I could do more to gain the hearts and minds of the Vietnamese, as they say."

"It won't be a long time or too long, as you said about the rabbi and the kid, after he cut his balls."

"No, he didn't castrate him, Phillips. He just circumcised him."

"Well, whatever he did it had to hurt."

"Are you going to be around for a while, Phillips?"

"Yes, I'm staying here tonight."

Torres said, "Well, in that case, we'll have a beer tonight and see the movie. They have one of those movies about the Beatles, *The Yellow Submarine*. I saw it in Korea a long time ago. It's rock and roll. If I see it one more time, it can't hurt."

"Yeah, Torres! But I heard a gunnery sergeant has some X-rated flicks he's going to show. I want to see some of that."

"Oh, you sex maniacs. I'll probably watch anyway, although it won't be long before I'll be back home."

"You lucky rascal. I hope nobody is keeping my old lady warm. I'm just kidding; she's a wonderful woman. You asked me about Oshiro. He's working at the maintenance shop of the armored unit. He advises them in the maintenance of tracks and weapons care. You'll see him. I'll let him know you're here. Next time when he stops, he may see you."

"Well, Phillips, I'll see you about 1900 hours, and we'll have that drink. I'll pay."

"Okay, pal. I can hardly wait to see that flick."

Torres walked in through the mess hall door, picked up a tray, and proceeded to select his food.

The evening hours came and Torres, after taking a bath, went to eat supper, as he had customarily been doing, at the mess hall. He walked back afterwards and listened to some country music and some favorites sung by the Kingston Trio. In his room he had a tape recorder, and some of the other military personnel had loaned him some tapes. He liked to hear Peter, Paul, and Mary singing ballads; he wished he could learn the music and see the trio in person sometime.

At 1950 hours he walked out of his room and headed for the club. He found Phillips eagerly waiting for the small club to open. A marine gunnery sergeant came and opened the small building.

"Come in, fellows. We don't have heavy stuff here, just a

215

couple of cases of beer. Anyway, we aren't allowed to get drunk. This is a combat zone and you know regulations."

The gunnery sergeant said, "It's okay with me. My friend Torres here is paying for a couple of beers. I came to see the flick you have."

"Oh, yeah! I brought it from Hong Kong. We'll be seeing it out on the patio. We'll put up a white sheet. You can drink your Ballantines while enjoying it. Bring a chair from your room. No charge; it's free. We just have to wait until dark so that we can see it on the drive-in screen, as we say here. No girls allowed, please."

Everyone laughed, including six or seven more guys who had come in.

The marine sergeant walked out to prepare the screen for the evening show. He got everything ready, then he invited everyone who wanted to watch the films to come in. He would be showing the X-rated film first and then the Beatles.

The show started and some of the fellows started to make comments about other films that were better. Suddenly the film broke, and some guys started to do cat calls and whistles. The marine sergeant said, "Guys, if you don't like it, it's not my fault. This film has been all over Vietnam already. It's had a lot of use."

There was a brief silence in which everyone could hear squeaky noises and giggles. The noises came from the other side the fence, which was made of cement and had concertina wires extended to the top to prevent outside infiltrators from getting in. Everyone wondered what was causing the noise. The marine sergeant got a ladder and climbed up to check the other side of the fence. They were all anxious and hoped it was nothing bad. The marine sergeant climbed down the ladder and said, "You know, fellows, we have to cancel the show."

"Why?" some guys complained.

"Well, my friends, it seems that we have a larger audience than we anticipated. There are about fifty mamasans and kids of all ages watching the movie from outside. I didn't realize that the sheet I put up is too high. The reflection of the camera focused on the screen goes through it and you can see the film from the other side. Do you hear them yelling. Mamasans and babysans all yelling 'Boom, boom, boom, boom.' They must think we're sex perverts. No more flicks, people."

"Boo! Boo! Hey, Sarge, let's keep winning their hearts and minds," someone yelled from the group.

Everyone dispersed and Phillips said to Torres, "It had to happen to me. My luck."

"Don't worry, Phillips. You can go on R and R very soon and see all kinds of films."

"You're kidding if you think I'm going to watch films when I can do it for real in Japan, Hong Kong, or any other place I decide to go. No way will I be watching films. I'll be the superstar, Torres."

"I see. You'd better be careful."

"Okay, Torres. If you need anything, I'll come and see you tomorrow before I leave for the field."

"Good night, Phillips."

Each departed for their sleeping quarters. Torres started to write a letter to his family. He didn't want to tell them about the expected decoration until he was sure of it.

26

It was June 25th and the first sergeant called Torres at 0900 hours, when he was on his way to start his daily chores.

"Sergeant Torres, I have good news for you. Do you have a clean, pressed uniform? You're going to need it. Pick up a shiny helmet, pistol belt with buckles, and a blue scarf at the supply room."

"Am I going to be an honor guard, First Sergeant?"

"No, nothing like that. You're going to be standing in front of one. You're going to receive a very high decoration for bravery. You've earned it, and now you'll be rewarded for it. A general is coming from Chulai tomorrow morning, and he will pin it on you. So it's not the Bronze Star because that can be pinned on by field officers. When a general comes to pin on a medal, it's something big."

"Alright, First Sergeant. What do you want me to do?"

"Sergeant Torres, the ceremony will be in front of the Division Headquarters tomorrow at 1000 hours. There will be many high brass officers there, and I want you to look like Audie Murphy."

"Halt, First Sergeant! Not that much. He was something great and a good move star, too. I admire him even in death. He was really great."

"Well, Sergeant Torres, I want you to look sharp and smell good."

"Yeah, I'll use a can of perfume. I'll borrow it from the mamasan."

"No, Brut will do it. I'll pick you up or you can come to the orderly room about 0900 hours. We'll walk up to headquarters, and I'll drop you off there. I have to come back and do my work, you know."

"It's okay, First Sergeant. I can manage."

"Now, go to the supply room and get the stuff I told you. Get your boots shined, too; spit shined, that is."

Torres said, "You know, I may go out and get drunk tonight and go out there tomorrow with a hangover and red eyes like a mad bull. I'll say to the general if he asks me why I look so enraged that I just want to go out there and end this war, sir. I'm mad as hell."

"You'd better not drink and fall on your face in front of everyone tomorrow. You might not get a medal after all."

"Okay, First Sergeant. I'll be ready by 0900."

"Good. I'll see you tomorrow. If you need anything, let me know today."

"Thanks, First Sergeant."

"You're welcome, hero."

"Humph, that sounds like a Philadelphia sandwich."

The first sergeant laughed and went his way, while Torres walked to the supply room to pick up the equipment he needed for the ceremony. He didn't know what kind of medal he was going to get, but even if he didn't get one, he was now happy that he'd come out alive and the rest of the fellows had not gotten hurt. Now he could write a letter home and tell them about it. He'd do it tonight and mail it early in the morning before the ceremony.

Torres walked back to his room with the three items he needed: the pistol belt, the shiny helmet, and the blue scarf. He checked for one of the uniforms the mamasan had pressed for him and also checked his shiny, spit-polished boots. After he finished, he walked to the resupply office.

As Torres entered his office, his assistant said, "Congratulations, Boss. I heard the news. You're getting a medal tomorrow. I'm glad for you. You deserve it. Nobody can take it away from you."

"Thanks, Martin. I should take the day off. You can manage by yourself."

"In fact, Boss, I give you the day off. You also deserve that. Everyone is happy out there. You've done a good job here, too."

"With your help. I have to give you the credit. You've been a great assistant and can manage by yourself. You taught me almost everything in here, Martin. I really do appreciate it."

"Well, if I can help, why shouldn't I. Let's see what we have for today. We can fill the requests and send them out.

"Don't worry, Boss. As I said, you can take your time off and get ready for your coronation."

"As if I were king."

"King for a day, Boss."

"You know, Martin, in here you have to keep up the good humor. Time goes faster and the days seem shorter."

"I know. I have four more months to do."

"You don't have that much time left."

"Well, Boss, it's not that much. I am only a Spec 4 and you're an E7. Very shortly you'll be an E8, a first sergeant with a diamond in the center. It must be nice to be sitting behind a desk telling everyone where to go and what to do."

"It's not that easy, Martin. There's always a boss of higher grade everywhere telling you what to do. You can count on that."

"I know, Boss. I was only kidding."

After lunch Torres went to see Martin. "I'm going to do a last minute check of my gear for tomorrow. There's not much to be done here."

"It's okay, Sergeant Torres. Everything is taken care of. I'll see you later."

Torres went to his room and started to write home. "My Dear Wife and Daughters: Tomorrow they have scheduled me to receive a medal in a brief ceremony. I don't know what medal it's going to be. I want you to know that I'm glad I'm leaving soon. I hope the girls keep doing good in school, as always. Best regards to all, and kisses and hugs to you. Love, Papy."

It was 0900 hours when the jeep's driver came to Torres's room. He knocked at the door. "Sarge, the first sergeant sent me here to check on how you're doing. He'll be waiting for you at 0950 hours. When you're ready to go, go to the orderly room. He'll be waiting there."

Torres opened the door and, looking at the name tag, asked, "You're the new driver?"

"Yes, I am. I replaced Spec 4 Stephens; he went home last week. My name is Sanders."

"Glad to know you, Sanders. I know you'll do a good job."

"I'm a private first class and may get promoted soon to Spec 4."

"You will, Sanders. Do a good job and don't take any unnecessary chances."

"Congratulations to you, Sergeant. You're getting a medal this morning. You must have done something out of the ordinary out there."

"Well, I did my job. I did my share, Sanders."

"I'll see you, Sarge. I must go back and tell the first sergeant that you're almost ready."

"Oh, no. I am ready; I'll be right behind you."

The driver walked away. Torres grasped his steel helmet after putting on his belt and walked to the shower room to put on the blue scarf and adjust his helmet in the mirror. After he finished, he walked over to the orderly room.

"Good, Sergeant Torres. You look sharp. That's the way to go. No we'll walk to Division Headquarters and meet the colonel

221

up there. They should be waiting for us, although we're early. It's better to be on time anyway."

The men started to walk, the first sergeant briefing Torres on the way.

"You'll be briefed by the adjutant and whoever is in charge of the ceremony. There's not much to do except stand tall out there."

"Alright, First Sergeant. Will do."

The two walked through the front gate of the compound and reached the 2nd Division ARVN Headquarters. The area was well cleaned and polished. You could really tell when a general was coming to camp. There was a flag-bearer detail standing by. It was composed of six men. One carried the American colors, one the Vietnamese national flag, one the 2nd ARVN Division colors, and the other carried the MACV command standard. The other two men were honor guards, standing to the side of the flag bearers. They were all U.S. Army personnel.

Torres was told by the first sergeant to wait at the front of the building. He stood by the short steps and waited for further orders. The first sergeant came out of the building accompanied by a first lieutenant. "Sergeant Torres, I'm the adjutant. I'll brief you."

Torres gave him a military salute. The officer acknowledged it and saluted back. The first sergeant said, "I must go. It's all yours, Lieutenant. I'll see you, Sergeant Torres. Good luck."

"Thanks, First Sergeant." said the lieutenant. The first sergeant walked away after saluting him courteously. The officer returned the salute.

The adjutant briefed Torres in a few minutes and showed him where he was supposed to stand and what to he was to do when a major walked out to bring him forward to be decorated on the command "People to be decorated, center, march." Torres had experience from previous ceremonies and it wouldn't be the last. He might have to attend ceremonies for other people in the future.

"The ceremony will not take more than twenty minutes, Sergeant Torres. The general will be here any minute. I see the other staff officers coming out now. Be ready and move to your post out there."

Torres walked out to the front yard, and the colors and escort took up their positions. The officers who had walked out of Division Headquarters came and lined themselves up. A roaring of a chopper was heard. It was the general arriving from Chulai. A brigadier general. The adjutant took his post and everything was ready to start right on time, 1050 hours.

The colonel walked over, met the general, and courteously saluted and shook hands. The general's field adjutant walked at the general's side. There was not too much fanfare, but it was well organized and prepared. Torres stood tall out in the yard. It was a bright day, with sunlight lighting the area. Some coconut palms were waving in the breeze. It was a nice day for a ceremony.

"Attention! Present arms!" The command followed in sequence. The general aligned himself with the colonel to his left. The major walked out at the command, "Persons to be decorated—center—march."

The adjutant sounded off, "Attention to orders." He continued, "General orders number 1806, award of the Silver Star. The following award is announced. Torres-Gonzales, Porfirio." The social security number followed and then the award designation, the Silver Star. "Date of Action, 31 January 1968. Theater: The Republic of Vietnam. Reason: For gallantry in action. Sergeant Torres-Gonzales distinguished himself by gallantry in action on 31 January 1968, while serving as light weapons infantry advisor, 4th Battalion, 5th Regiment, 2nd Infantry Division, Army of the Republic of Vietnam. On that date, the battalion was attacked by an estimated two Vietcong main forces battalions. With no thought for his own safety, Sergeant Torres-Gonzales began spotting targets and directing fire on the enemy."

Hold it! Directing fire on what? I was the only one firing. I was alone. I'd realized I was alone.

It continued: "The enemy had closed within two hundred yards. The volume of fire intensified, and the Vietnamese troops began a withdrawal."

What withdrawal? They weren't out there. Nobody was out there except me.

It continued: "Sergeant Torres held his position to provide cover for the battalion."

They're right. I held my position. There was no choice but to provide cover, but for whom? To provide myself a chance to survive and come out as best I could.

It continued: "As a direct result of his bravery, the Vietnamese were able to assault and regain their original position."

Come on! This is too much. Torres's thoughts could not understand. Maybe his ears were playing games. He'd cleaned them this morning.

The announcement continued: "Moving with the leading elements..."

What leading elements? I was charging the enemy by myself. No one was even near until two young soldiers popped out and saw me, joining me at the end when the Vietcong were running for their lives. Many things passed through Torres's mind.

The orders continued: "Sergeant Torres not only delivered effective fire on the enemy but also administered first aid to the wounded Vietnamese soldiers."

There is some truth in this order. I did hold my position, I delivered effective fire, and I administered first aid to wounded soldiers. Torres did not care about the rest. It wasn't the truth—the *real* truth. He'd wait and read it later. Maybe they were reading the wrong orders.

It concluded: "Authority by direction of the President under the provisions of the Act of Congress, approved 9 July 1918. Signed, Sidney Gritz, Colonel, U.S.A., Adjutant General for the

Commander Walter T. Kerwin, Jr., Major General, U.S.A. Chief of Staff."

The general walked over to where Torres was standing by. A captain opened a box and the general reached in, pulled out a medal, and pinned it on the left lapel of Torres's jacket. He said, "Congratulations, Sergeant."

The general shook hands and Torres gave him a military salute, but with a somber look on his face. He felt proud of getting a medal, but it should have been for the right reasons. The colonel, who was standing to the left of the general, also shook Torres's hand and congratulated him.

The general walked away and returned to his waiting chopper, his field adjutant walking at his side. Torres watched as the general walked away, with his spit-shined belt and a holster carrying a nacred pistol.

Everyone dispersed soon after the general was out of sight. Torres did an about-face. As he started to walk back to the compound, he saw the colonel, who approached him and then said, "Congratulations once more, Sergeant Torres."

Torres did not answer and kept walking toward the compound, his mind on the orders he was reading.

Why? He wasn't out there. I was out there myself. Maybe I was recommended for a Bronze Star or a Commendation Medal and it was upgraded. Torres felt discouraged, but he would keep his medal because it was a medal and at least there were some facts that were true on the orders. He would talk about it and set the record straight. Even if no one believed him. He felt that the many people he knew and trusted would believe him. His family and close relatives would believe him. His friends would believe him. He'd never been controversial, but he had to tell the truth.

Torres took off the medal and placed it back in the case before he reached the compound gate. He went to his room and put away the medal; then he took the shiny helmet, belt, and scarf and walked to the supply room to turn them in. The supply sergeant said, "Cheer up, Sarge. Congratulations on your decoration. It's nice to have a hero between us."

"Thanks, Sergeant. Thanks for the equipment."

He walked back to the resupply office. His assistant immediately said, "Horray for my boss. What did you get?"

"They handed me a medal, Martin. You know, sometimes people get discouraged and their mood changes."

"I see you look kind of sad. After a ceremony and standing in front of high brass with everyone looking at you, you should be happier."

"Well, tell me, Martin. How would you feel if someone gave you something and the purpose for it was all wrong?"

"What do you mean, Sarge?" Martin asked.

"You see, let me show you the orders and read the citation. Half is true and half is wrong, and it's the wrong half that bothers me. Not that I should get something higher than a Silver Star; but even if I got a Commendation Medal, it should state the truth."

"Let me see. Wow! It's really sad and I don't blame you for feeling discouraged. But, Sarge, don't worry. People who know you respect you for who you are. You're a good person and nobody can change that, unless you want to change yourself. Chin up! Keep the medal. Just remember what you did, what your conscience dictated to you, and know that you did the right thing. You didn't come here for medals and neither did I."

"You're right, young man. Well, let's wait for my day to go back. It's close. I'm getting so short my underwear doesn't fit anymore. I may have to borrow mamasan's pants."

"They'll only fit you in one leg, Sarge."

Torres's somber mood changed, and both men laughed.

"Remember, boss, keep your chin up and don't let anything bother you."

"By the way, Martin, they even misspelled my name and my second last name, also.

"Your name is Porfirio, right?"

"Yes, there're not many of us around, but some were very famous. Porfirio Diaz, a Mexican president a long time ago, and Porfirio Rubirosa from the Dominican Republic, who married the president's daughter and later on married Barbara Hutton, a rich girl. He was a playboy and was killed in a car crash."

"You should get assignment orders very shortly, Sarge," Martin stated.

"By next week."

"I'll bet you can hardly wait to get back."

"You bet right," said Torres.

27

It was Thursday morning when Torres went to his assigned job and saw a familiar face walking toward the mess hall.

"Hello, hello, hello, short-timer. I saw Phillips the other day and he told me you're working in the maintenance section of the armored unit. You're advising them how to keep the tracks running," said Torres.

Oshiro replied, "Yes, my friend, it won't be too long before we leave this place. I get bored in the shop. Sometimes I wish I would be going back to the field."

Torres said, "No way, pal. You'd better play it safe and stay where you are. You don't need medals. You did what you came to do and very shortly it will be time to go home."

"I heard you got the Silver Star the other day."

"Yeah, but I wish the citation stated the truth."

"What did it say?"

"It says that I was directing fire on the enemy, that I covered the withdrawal of the battalion, and that I had joined the attacking forces. It's not true, Oshiro. I was on my own out there and started the counterattack by myself. Nobody was with me until the end when two binshis came over, saw me, and helped. I'll never forget when I reached the corner of that zinc building and started to scream and fire my carbine. The Vietcong dispersed like a flock of birds flying out of a bush who'd been caught by surprise. They ran in all directions."

"Well, you know what you did, and you can tell the whole world about it. There's an operation coming tomorrow and they asked me if I wanted to go. I volunteered. It's safe; the tracks have a lot of protection."

"You what? Come on, pal. You don't have time to fool around like that. You did your time out there already. Let someone else go. Oh, man, you really surprise me. No place is safe in war. I remember when I was in Korea during the war and I was on my way home. We were in the replacement center waiting to leave the next day. At night we heard a zooming noise and two loud explosions. A Mig had gotten through. The radar apparently didn't detect it. It dropped two bombs at one end of the camp. I jumped into a foxhole and didn't come out until the next day. I did not take any chances."

"I'll be okay, Torres."

"I hope so, pal. Be careful."

"I'll see you, friend. You got your orders already?"

"Yeah, I'm going to Dix. That's what I wanted. We may go on the same trip back together."

"I hope so."

"Remember, friend, not even the presidential palace is safe. Keep your head low. I'll see you."

Torres walked away, shaking his head and saying to himself, "Sixteen days to go and he volunteers. It's crazy. I hope nothing happens."

The day passed. That night the sound of artillery and automatic machine-gun fire could be heard coming from the northwest and up in the hills. The next day there was calm as usual, but again at night the gun noises intensified. It sounded like all hell had broken loose. The high hills were illuminated by flares and Spooky flying around firing rockets and machine guns. Torres thought about Oshiro. He prayed that he'd get back okay.

Early the next morning, about 0850 hours, Torres walked over to get a cup of coffee at the mess hall. As he reached the mess hall side door, he heard some armored personnel carriers and tanks moving on the dirt road in front of the compound. He walked over and saw Phillips jumping out of a personnel carrier. His mood was somber and agitated. Torres went over to greet him.

"Hi, Phillips. I hope everything is okay. I saw Oshiro two days ago, and he said he was going out there for the last time."

"Oh, Torres. I don't know. I just hate to tell you."

"He didn't make it. He's in that truck back there. He's inside a rubber bag.

"Oh, no-o-o-o-!"

"Yes, Torres. He was killed."

Torres's eyes filled with tears as he walked over to check the truck moving by him on the way to the hospital or Grave Registration Center. It was a very sad day for Torres. He walked back to the compound and said to Martin, "I'll be in my room if you need me."

"Okay, Sarge. Don't worry." Martin did not know about Torres's friend's death.

Torres walked back and listened to Peter, Paul, and Mary singing "Blowing in the Wind." He played it over and over until he fell asleep. He didn't even bother to open the door and let mamasan in to clean his room and take care of his laundry. Seven days. Sixteen days. Perhaps destiny. In Torres's mind he thought about a childhood friend named Joseph Rodriguez, who'd gone to California. Torres was eleven years old and Jose was twelve. Jose had said to him, "Life is the greatest school. You learn through experience. But in order to get something out of it, you must live it."

How right he'd been. Torres never got to see him again, although they wrote each other for some time.

It was early September when Torres was called to the orderly room by the company clerk. "Sergeant Torres, you know your assignment and I received your departure order—working with trainees at Fort Dix. You like that and that's what you got. You'll be a first sergeant there because your promotion orders are coming shortly. You may get them before you leave next week. I'll give them to you as soon as I receive them."

"Thanks, Specialist. I like my assignment."

The clerk said, "To each his own. I like to work with paperwork, computers and typewriters."

"I think I'm going to be a teacher when I retire from the military," said Torres.

Martin said, "You're leaving next week, and your replacement is in. You'll meet him this morning. He was out there like you. Now he's getting a break also. You can brief him, and your assistant can do the rest. By the way, the first sergeant wants to see you. Wait for him. He's talking to the captain now. He's got something to give you."

Torres sat down in a wooden chair. Ten minutes later the first sergeant walked out of the commander's office. He had in his hands a certificate. The commander also walked out and said to Torres, "Hello, Sergeant Torres. The first sergeant has a certificate for you. You have done a good job."

The first sergeant handed Torres the certificate and Torres read the heading. "The Senior Advisor awards this Certificate of Appreciation to SFC Torres for Distinguished Service as Light Infantry Advisor and Resupply Non-Commissioned Officer for Advisory Team Two."

He said to the commander and the first sergeant, "Thank you, sir. Thank you, First Sergeant." He saluted the captain. After being recognized, he made an about-face and walked out of the room.

He continued to read the citation written on the certificate, which concluded, "During the period 25 September 1967 to 22 September 1968, his sound guidance and counsel and his personal example of behavior under enemy fire was an inspiration to his associates and the Vietnamese soldiers whom he advised." *At least, this one states the truth,* he thought.

28

The day came and Torres got up early. He went around and said good-bye to the people he knew and wished them the best. He said to Martin, "You know, Martin, I really appreciated working with you. I may see you in the future. Good luck and the best to you, my friend. You made my job easier here and I won't forget it. If you ever get around to Fort Dix, look me up."

"Thank you, Sergeant Torres. It's been very rewarding working with you. The best to you. When you get back to the world, show your medals without remorse; you earned them."

"I was given a Certificate of Appreciation a couple of days ago, and it means a lot to me."

"You received the third highest decoration. Although some of what it says isn't true, the medal is still yours. Wear it proudly, Sarge."

"Good-bye, Martin."

Torres walked out and loaded his equipment into the rear seat of the jeep. He was then driven to the airport. Sanders said, while driving down the dirt road, "Sarge, I made specialist four yesterday."

"Congratulations, I knew you could do it."

"Sure, you told me. You're going now to Da Nang and then Saigon. I wish I was going with you."

"Well, your time will come. Take care of yourself and be careful. Don't take any chances."

"Alright, First Sergeant. I know you got your orders also. You'll be in charge of a company and working in an office back in the States. It will be good for you."

"Thanks, Specialist Sanders."

Torres stepped out of the vehicle as it came to a halt in front of the bleachers at the airport. A short time later the courier plane arrived. Torres, with Sanders's help, loaded his equipment, climbed aboard the craft, and waved his hand to Sanders, who stayed and waited for the plane to take off. Torres leaned back and relaxed.

The plane landed at Da Nang Airport after stopping and picking up some other passengers who were mostly going on R and R leaves. There were some going on emergency leaves back to the United States.

A military bus picked up the passengers at the airport and brought them to the same MACV compound Torres had arrived at before. The out-processing took two days; then Torres was flown to Saigon for further out-processing, which also took two days.

Torres departed Saigon on a commercial flight. He arrived at San Francisco Airport after a short stop at the Philippines. He continued his journey. After a stopover in Atlanta, he arrived at Miami International Airport. In four hours he would be back in San Juan and at his brother-in-law's, who would drive him to Fort Buchanan, where Elsa and the girls were waiting impatiently.

The American Airlines jet landed. Torres, after debarking and walking down the aisle to pick up his baggage, met his brother-in-law Gilberto. Gilberto's nickname was Gilo. Gilo said, "Hello there. I'm glad you're back. Everyone is waiting for you. Mayi [Elsa's nickname] and the girls are waiting. I'll take you to them as soon as we get the baggage."

"Gilo, I'm so happy to see you. The trip was good all the way."

"You look great. And now you have one more stripe on your shoulder. You got high decorations. It's great. Everyone is happy.

233

"The newspaper knows about your deeds and a reporter named Ramon Rodriguez wants to interview you tomorrow. He'll be waiting at the office in old San Juan. I'll drive you there; it should not take too long."

"Well, I'd like that. I'd like to tell them the truth, as things happened."

"Just tell him what you think."

Torres arrived home, and Elsa and the girls happily embraced him. Elsa cried and said, "I prayed every day for your safe return. I thank the Good Lord for it." She kissed him. The girls joined them, and they all embraced.

The next day Gilo came to pick up Torres and said, "Let's go. I called Ramon at his office. He's waiting; he's supposed to be a good reporter."

The two men left. When they arrived at the newspaper office, Torres walked up to the second floor, where Mr. Rodriguez had his office along with other reporters.

Torres said, "Sir, I can only say that I predict a quick solution to the end of the war. It doesn't make any difference which type of government takes over Vietnam. Their way of life will be hard to change. Their culture has prevailed for years, and it won't be easy to make them change. They are a peaceful people, and by tradition and custom so they will remain. I'm very pleased with the hospitality they showed me and all the attention. I hope the war comes to an end soon."

The reporter asked about his citations and Torres, being discreet said, "You know what they used to call me?"

"What?"

"They used to call me Co-Van. Yes, Da Co-Van."

"And what does it mean?"

"Sir, it means the advisor."